GW00584796

THE
ROYAL SEA BATHING HOSPITAL
MARGATE
Founded 1791

PATRON
HER MAJESTY, QUEEN ELIZABETH II

Previous Patrons

HM King George IV
(from when he was Prince of Wales)
HM King William IV
HM Queen Victoria
HM King Edward VII
HM King George V
HM King George VI

Sir William James Erasmus Wilson. This full-length statue stands in the forecourt of the Royal Sea Bathing Hospital facing the ward block and chapel which he built. Behind may be seen the four-storey Nurses' Home.

THE HISTORY
of the
ROYAL SEA BATHING HOSPITAL
MARGATE
1791 – 1991

by
F.G. ST CLAIR STRANGE, FRCS

With a chapter on the
League of Friends of the Royal Sea Bathing Hospital

by
P.R. WRIGHT, FRCS

and
A Note on the Chapel

by
T.G. THOMAS, FRCS

MERESBOROUGH BOOKS

Published by Meresborough Books, 17 Station Road, Rainham, Kent. ME8 7RS.

Further copies of this book are available from the Hospital, from your local bookshop or by post from Meresborough Books. Please add £1.30 towards inland postage costs, £2.50 overseas.

© Copyright 1991. F.G. St Clair Strange

All royalties from the sale of this book will be donated to hospital charities.

ISBN 0948193 573

Printed by Biddles Ltd., Guildford.

CONTENTS

Margate in the eighteenth century.

Turner's picture of Margate, taken from a point almost exactly outside the hospital.

6

Preface

It is a delightful activity to delve into aged records and extract a story from them such as the History of the Royal Sea Bathing Hospital. I only hope that reading it will provide as much pleasure.

One or two preliminary remarks are necessary. For example, certain paragraphs in the narrative may seem to be rather staccato. But it must be remembered that these are items from the records and present all that is known of the episode. No attempt has been made to embroider such extracts because this would only introduce fancy and padding and spoil the factual record which is history. So the bare reference is left to stand on its own.

It should be appreciated that, simply because a person is said to have been a patient in the Royal Sea Bathing Hospital, this does not imply that he or she was suffering from any particular disease.

Picture Credits

The Administrative Director of *L'Hôpital Orthopédique de la Suisse Romande.*

Dr R. Andrews

Barracuda Books Ltd. and Mrs Scurrell.

Le Bibliothécaire de l'Académie de Médicine de Paris.

Mrs Edgar Freshman.

The Isle of Thanet Gazette (the late Mike Featle).

The Daily Mirror.

William Heinemann Medical Books Ltd.

Mr Milton-Worssell.

Professor A. Mounier-Kuhn.

The Thanet District Council.

The Trustees of the British Museum.

Messrs Whitbread Ltd.

The engraving of the "Medley" picture is amongst the Hospital Archives but the original is the property of the Medical Society of London and hangs in its House in Chandos Street.

Most of the other illustrations are either in the Archives of the Royal Sea Bathing Hospital or are the property of the author, including all the illustrations in colour not previous acknowledged.

Photographs of members of the staff of the Royal Sea Bathing Hospital, including some now retired, have been supplied by themselves.

Every effort has been made to trace owners of copyright material, both literary and pictorial, but this has not always been successful. If copyright has been inadvertently infringed, it is hoped that a full apology, which is here offered, will be accepted.

Acknowledgements

Special acknowledgements are due in two instances. The first would be to the late Miss Olive Monahan, for thirty-two years Assistant Matron of the Royal Sea Bathing Hospital. She was an enthusiastic student of the history of the Hospital and assembled many memorabilia which have facilitated writing this story and made it a very pleasant task.

The second is to Dr John Whyman, Ph.D., of the University of Kent at Canterbury. One of the chapters in his Ph.D. Thesis "Aspects of Holiday-Making and Resort Development within the Isle of Thanet, with particular reference to Margate, circa 1736 to circa 1840" was devoted to the early history of the Royal Sea Bathing Hospital. It contains a fund of information and interest and was based on far-reaching and meticulous research, and I am most grateful to him for permission to make a number of quotations from it.

Both Mr P.R. Wright, FRCS, retired Consulting Orthopaedic Surgeon to the Hospital and Miss Shirley Bowskill, SRN, ONC, currently a Sister at the Hospital, have been of the greatest help in advice and in the search for and provision of essential and interesting details on innumerable occasions and my warmest thanks are their due.

Mr T. Glyn Thomas has provided a concise but informative contribution on the chapel, which really needs a whole book to itself, and to him I am most grateful.

I should also like to thank colleagues and members and ex-members of the staff of the Royal Sea Bathing Hospital for giving me outlines of the work of their departments and eyewitness memories and anecdotes. My thanks are due to Sue Cover, Librarian of the Kent Post-Graduate Medical Centre at Canterbury, for help in retrieving references, to Miss MacIntosh for advice regarding publication, to Aaron Smith Studios, Ramsgate, for help in photographic reproductions and to Lanes (East Kent) for providing stationery.

I should like to thank the following for permission to refer to or quote from publications which are fully documented in the references:
The Administrative Director of *L'Hôpital Orthopédique de la Suisse Romande* for Hughli, J. and Nicod. L. *"Centième Anniversaire de l'Hôpital Orthopédique de la Suisse Romand"*.
La Bibliothécaire de l'Académie de Médecine de Paris for Cazin, H. *"L'Influence des Bains de Mer sur la Scrofule des Enfants"*.
Jonathan Cape, for de Kruif, P. "Men Against Death".

9

Messrs Collins, for Marsden, C. "The English at the Seaside".

William Heinemann Medical Books, for Abraham, J.J. "Lettsom, His Life, Times, Friends and Descendants".

Hillier, Caroline, for "The Bulwark Shore, Thanet and the Cinque Ports". Eyre, Methuen, 1980 and Paladin Books, 1982.

Editor, the Isle of Thanet Gazette, for references to editions in 1926, 1946 and 1970.

Editor of the Journal of Bone and Joint Surgery, for references to articles by Charnley, J. and McKee, G.K., and to Mr McKee.

MacMillan & Co., for Jerrold, W. "Highways and Byways in Kent" and for McLelland, D. "Karl Marx, his Life and Thought". Also for "Poems", by W.E. Henley.

Madden, P. for "Just Like That", Production on Channel 4 Television.

Medical History, for Hadley, R.M. "Life and Times of Sir William James Erasmus Wilson 1809-1884", and to Mr Hadley.

The Medical Society of London for Thomas, T.G. "The Character of Erasmus Wilson", and to Mr Thomas.

The Daily Mirror for Ashcroft, Eileen "Sincerity".

Penguin Books, for Newman, N. "North-East and East Kent".

The President and Council of the Royal College of Surgeons of England for Cope, Z. "The History of the Royal College of Surgeons of England".

Spiers, John, Hassocks Flare Books, for Gilbert, E.M. "Brighton, Old Ocean's Bauble".

The Editor, the Sunday Times Colour Supplement, for Connor, P. "Cleopatra's Needle".

The Editor, The Daily Telegraph for "An Invalid", "Margate in Winter".

The Editor, The Times, for Howard, P. "The Needle starts a new Century".

Unwin Hyman, for Heyerdahl, T. "Aku, Aku".

I very much appreciate so many people who give their permission to use their copyright material accompanying it with their best wishes for successful publication.

Finally, I should like to thank my secretary, Mrs Godden, for her help and Mrs Shaw, the Area Archivist, also John Hippisley, Keith Attwood and Phil White of Shell and Hamish Mackay Miller of Meresborough Books for all their generous help in publication.

10

Sponsors

Grateful thanks are due to the following who have generously contributed to the costs of publication of this History.

Dr Ray Andrews, MD, FRCP.
The Worshipful Company of Barbers.
Barclays Bank Ltd., Margate.
Dr R. Barter, MA, MD, FRCPI, D.Phys.Med.
Nigel Blackburn, Esq., FRCS.
Michael Butler, Esq., FRCS.
R.F. Cant, Esq., MB, B.Ch., DMRD(Ed).
The Canterbury & Thanet District Health Authority.
The Worshipful Company of Clothworkers (Clothworkers' Foundation).
F.D.C. Cobb, Esq.
M. Conybeare, Esq., FRCS.
Maurice Down, Esq., OBE.
Dr Ann Ferguson, FFARCS.
The Worshipful Company of Goldsmiths.
The Worshipful Company of Grocers.
The Halifax Building Society.
Howmedica Ltd., London.
Johnson and Johnson Orthopaedics Ltd., New Milton.
Dr Roger Kirkpatrick, FFARCS
D.J. Klugman, Esq., FRCS.
The League of Friends of the Royal Sea Bathing Hospital.
The Worshipful Company of Mercers.
The late Barton Morgan, Esq.
Sir James Mount, CBE.
Pfizers Ltd., Sandwich.
Portex Ltd., Hythe.
K.J. Rawlings, Esq., FCII, FBIBA.
The Royal Insurance Company.
Sally Line, Ramsgate.
S.E. Co-Operative Society, Kent Branch Committee.
Shell Research, Sittingbourne.
Mr and Mrs Peter Sparrow.
I.B.M. Stephen, Esq., FRCS.
Arthur Stevens, Esq.
Mrs Arthur Stevens, JP, SRN, ONC.
Charles F. Thackeray Ltd., Leeds.
T. Glyn Thomas, Esq., FRCS.
Dr R.H. Withrington, MD, FRCP.
P.R. Wright, Esq., FRCS.

Grateful thanks are also due to a great many members of the staff of the Royal Sea Bathing Hospital and others who have made pre-publication payments for their copies of this History.

F.G. St Clair Strange

The Royal Sea Bathing Hospital, Margate, 1947.

Chapter 1
THE FOUNDATION

The Royal Sea Bathing Hospital at Margate is believed to be the oldest Orthopaedic Hospital in the world. It was founded by Dr John Coakley Lettsom on 2nd July 1791.

It is true that there was, at one time, a so-called hospital for treatment of skeletal deformities which had been founded in 1779 in Switzerland at Orbe, by a physician of Geneva, Dr Jean André Venel. But in the accepted sense, it was not exactly a hospital, Dr Venel taking children, mostly suffering from scoliosis, into his own home for treatment. In 1791 he handed the work on to his nephew, Dr P.F. Jaccard, who continued the work in his own home until 1820, having removed, in the interval to Aubonne. But then the "hospital" ceased to have any real existence. It was not until fifty-six years later, in 1876, that *L'Hôpital Orthopédique de la Suisse Romande* was founded at Lausanne and incorporated the orthopaedic tradition of Dr Venel (see appendix 1 to this chapter),

In the island of Little Jost van Dyke, off Tortola in the Virgin Islands, in the year 1744 a Mrs Mary Lettsom, née Coakley, the wife of a Quaker, gave birth to her seventh pair of male twins. None of the previous twelve boys had survived but this pair did so and one of them was John Coakley Lettsom. He grew up to study Medicine at Edinburgh and London and qualified as a doctor at the age of twenty-one. After practising in Jamaica for six months, when he earned the astonishing sum of £2,000, Lettsom returned to England and became the foremost medical man in London of that period (Abraham, 1933).

Apart from his medical work, Lettsom was a man of very many parts. He was a famous botanist and planted two botanical gardens in London, he introduced the mangel-wurzel into England and popularised tea-drinking. Lettsom was a true philanthropist and, among his other activities, was a great prison reformer, one of the founders of the Royal Humane Society and a strong protagonist of Jenner. Indeed, from Lettsom's grandson the lymph was obtained for the vaccination of Queen Victoria.

Lettsom was also an expert gemmologist and when he presented his collection of rocks, stones and precious stones to the University of Cambridge, Massachusetts, it was acknowledged with the description that it was "by far the richest and most extensive collection of minerals in the United States".

John Coakley Lettsom, MD, LL.D, FRS, FAS, FRCP (Edinburgh), Founder of the Royal Sea Bathing Hospital.

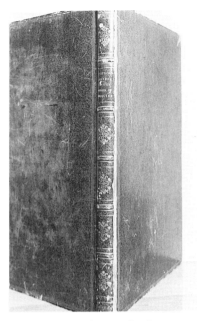

Lettsom's Anniversary Oration, cover.   Lettsom's Anniversary Oration, spine.

In 1773 Lettsom founded the Medical Society of London from which, some thirty-two years later, the Royal Society of Medicine was an offshoot. Lettsom gave the Medical Society of London its fifth Anniversary Oration in 1778 entitled: "History of the Origin of Medicine". This he published at the Society's request and presented a copy, with a manuscript covering letter in his own hand, to a Mr Henry Perkins. From him, through the hands of the late Dr C.T. Richardson, this volume and letter came into the possession of the Royal Sea Bathing Hospital.

Lettsom was a very successful doctor and became very rich. He is said to have earned £12,000 in 1800 (Pettigrew, 1817). In an attempt to equate this with today's values, it is recorded that the cost of feeding 127 patients for four weeks at that time was £100.17s.3d (RSBHA 359), the equivalent of 6¾d or 2.8p a day. At this sort of rate, his income would have been about £600,000 in the late 1980s. Income tax had been introduced by William Pitt in 1799. In 1800 it was two shillings in the pound on all incomes over £200, so that his net income would still have been the equivalent of over £540,000 per annum today. The tax was rescinded in 1801 but re-introduced from 1803-1816 to pay for the Napoleonic Wars and finally, by Peel in 1842, and was as low as 2d in the pound in the 1870s. Happy days!

15

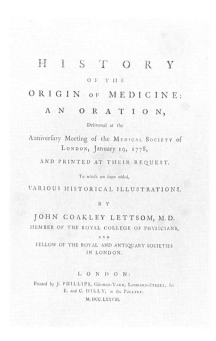

H I S T O R Y

OF THE

ORIGIN OF MEDICINE:

AN ORATION,

Delivered at the

Anniversary Meeting of the MEDICAL SOCIETY of
LONDON, January 19, 1778,

AND PRINTED AT THEIR REQUEST.

To which are since added,

VARIOUS HISTORICAL ILLUSTRATIONS.

BY

JOHN COAKLEY LETTSOM, M.D.
MEMBER OF THE ROYAL COLLEGE OF PHYSICIANS,
AND
FELLOW OF THE ROYAL AND ANTIQUARY SOCIETIES
IN LONDON.

LONDON:

Printed by J. PHILLIPS, GEORGE-YARD, LOMBARD-STREET, for
E. and C. DILLY, in the POULTRY.
M. DCC. LXXVIII.

Lettsom's Anniversary Oration, title page.

Perkins' book-plate and Dr Richardson's card.

Lettsom was also a most generous person. In 1778 he presented the deeds of his house at Bolt Court in the City of London to the Medical Society of London in which to hold its meetings. The famous "Medley" picture shows him presenting the keys to the Society. The picture was painted in 1800 and engraved, by Nathan Bramwhite, in 1801. It is, in a sense, a fanciful picture because not all those in it could have been present. In fact, probably only four of those shown were actually there at the time.

At this point, we must go back a little farther into the seventeenth century. In 1660 a Dr Wittie promoted sea bathing "cures" at Scarborough in Yorkshire and, of course, as with all fashionable remedies, sea bathing came to be looked on as the cure for everything, from cancer to ruptures, from asthma to madness. Certainly sea bathing for pleasure was being practised

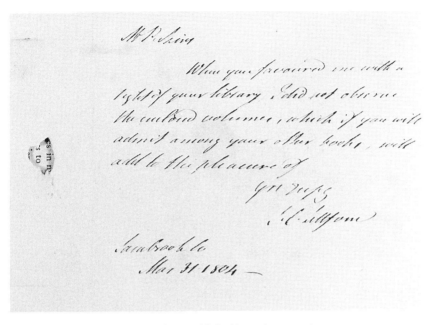

Lettsom's letter to Mr Perkins and autograph.

by the hardy Yorkshiremen at Scarborough by 1735 and, by 1753, at Margate, where the Quaker, Benjamin Beale, invented the machine "that robbed bathing of its original innocence, when nymphs could be seen cavorting naked in the waves and men dived in gamely from rowing boats" (Hillier, 1980).

In 1750 a certain Dr Richard Russell of London published his advocacy of sea bathing for health purposes (Russell, 1750). He did not limit this treatment to bathing only, but also recommended the drinking of small quantities of sea water as well. He also said that sea water made a good "dentifrice". Russell's publication was entitled *"De Tabe Glandulari sive de usu Aquae Marinae in Morbis Glandularum Dissertatio"*. Three years later he published an English text on the same subject (Russell, 1753). So effectively did he promulgate his theory that it soon became fashionable for the Court and Society to repair for sea bathing to the small south coast town of Brighthelmstone (now Brighton) and, in due course, for the Prince Regent to build his famous Pavilion there. As might be expected, Dr Russell earned the nickname "Sea-water Russell".

"At Brighton, gentlemen were still shivering and hesitating on the brink, 'their persons . . . wholly exposed', which practice remained 'a stain on the *gentility* of Brighthelmstonians', but at Margate, the bathing machines

17

The "Medley" picture. Dr J.C. Lettsom presents the Keys of Bolt Court to the Medical Society of London, 1778.
Back row, l to r: Edward Bancroft, Mr Ware, Thomas Bradley, James Sims, Edward Jenner, Mr Blair, William Babington. Seated, at left: Joseph Hart Myers, William Woodville, Nathaniel Hulme, Sayre Walker, Sir John McNamara Hayes. Seated centrally: Robert Hooper, Eward Ford. Lettsom standing in the centre. At right, back row, seated: John Haighton, Robert John Thornton, John Shadwell, John Aitkin. Front row: Charles Combe, John Relph, William Saunders. Jenner is said to have been added later and many of those pictured could not have been present at the time! (The picture was painted in about 1800 and was engraved by Nathan Bramwhite in 1801.)

18

Dr Richard "Sea-Water" Russell.

TABE GLANDULARI,

SIVE

DE USU AQUÆ MARINÆ

IN

MORBIS GLANDULARUM

DISSERTATIO.

Auctore RICARDO RUSSELL, M. D.

Θάλασσα κλύζει πάντα τ' ανθρώπων κακά.
Mare abluit omnia hominum mala.
Euripides Iphigen. in Taur. V. 1193.

E THEATRO SHELDONIANO,
Proſtant venales apud JACOBUM FLETCHER, Oxon. & J.
& J. RIVINGTON, Lond. MDCCL.

7 Title-page of the first edition of Dr. Russell's book on sea-water

Title page of Dr Russell's Dissertation.

lowered their hoods which were like folding versions of a prairie wagon, to encapsulate the bather in a salty privacy." (Hillier, l.c.)

Now Lettsom, the Quaker, had a very tender approach to the extreme poverty and disease which he found when he "quitted the spacious streets and squares" and penetrated into "the little alleys and courts", conditions which were "aggravated by the want of air and exercise" (Lettsom, 1801). There he "found a species of disease for which no suitable aid had till lately been afforded: for scrofulous disease . . . sea air and sea bathing are particularly requisite".

In consequence, he called together, on July 2nd 1791, a meeting of eight others beside himself, at the London Coffee House, Ludgate Hill, London.

It is a tremendous thrill to be able to read the actual manuscript minutes of this historic meeting, reproduced in full on the following pages.

It is noteworthy that these minutes are not written in the copperplate script of the trained amanuensis. There may not have been one at the meeting. So these minutes were probably written by one of the members present, most likely by Rev. John Pridden.

19

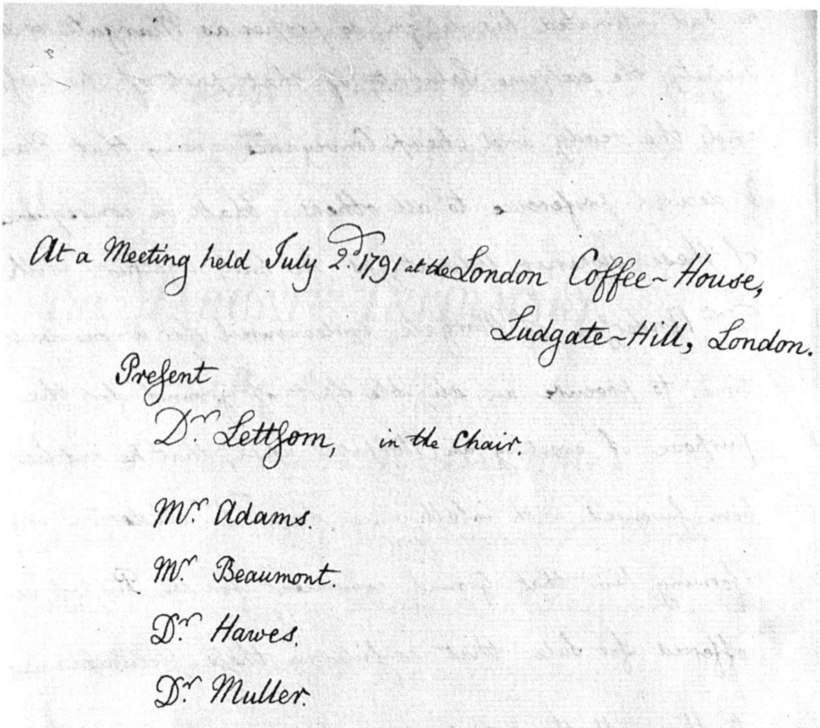

At a Meeting held July 2. 1791 at the London Coffee-House, Ludgate-Hill, London.

Present

Dr. Lettsom, in the Chair.

Mr. Adams.

Mr. Beaumont.

Dr. Hawes.

Dr. Muller.

Mr. Deputy Nichols.

Sr. John Peter.

Rev.d John Pridden.

Mr. J. R. Syms.

The Chairman informed the above Gentlemen, that he had requested their attendance to impart to them an Idea

he

Original Minutes

he had long formed of establishing a Receptacle for the
Relief of the Poor whose Diseases required Sea-Bathing;
that among the numerous places of Resort on the Sea-Coast
none appeared to him, as well as to several others to whom
he had intimated his design, so proper as Margate or its
Vicinity; the extreme Salubrity of that part of the Coast,
and the ready and cheap Conveyance thither, giving that Place
a decided preference to all others; that in consequence
of these superior Advantages, he had, together with
Dr. Anderson, of Margate, endeavoured for a considerable
time to procure an eligible Spot of Ground for the
purpose of erecting an Hospital upon; that he had lately
been favoured with intelligence from Dr. Anderson in=
=forming him that Ground convenient for the Purpose was
offered for Sale; that, considering these Circumstances,
together with the important and increasing Use of Sea-
-Bathing, and the utter inability of the Poor to
experience any Benefit from such a Remedy by the
Expence attending a distant Residence from their
Families and Occupations, he conceived no Opportu=
=nity so proper as the present for forming such an
Institution

Original Minutes

21

Institution for the Relief of the Poor and therefore he submitted to their Judgements what Procedure would be most efficacious to expedite the Formation and Establishment of such a valuable and much wanted Institution.

Resolved that the above Gentlemen together with John Milward, Esqr. Dr. William Saunders and Dr. James Sims, form a Committee for managing the Affairs of an Institution to be called

THE MARGATE INFIRMARY,

for the Relief of the Poor

whose Diseases require SEA~BATHING.

Resolved that this Society consist of a Patron, a President, Vice-Presidents, a Treasurer, a Secretary, Governors, a Collector and a Messenger.

Resolved that Dr. Lettsom be the Treasurer, and the Revd. Mr. Pridden be the Secretary to this Charity.

Resolved that Application be made to the Members for the County of Kent, and the Town and Port of Dover, for their Countenance in behalf of this Institution.

Resolved That Dr. Lettsom, Mr. Deputy Nichols and the Revd. Mr. Pridden be requested to view the ground offered for Sale, as soon as they conveniently can, and if it appears eligible for the Purpose to procure the same.

Resolved. That Subscriptions be solicited, and the following Address and Resolutions be printed for the Information of the Public.

MARGATE INFIRMARY.

THE great Importance of Sea-bathing having suggested to several Gentlemen the Propriety of erecting an Hospital on the Sea Coast for the Benefit of the Poor; a Meeting of the Well-wishers to such an Institution was held, on Saturday the 2d of July, at the London Coffee House, Dr. LETTSOM in the Chair; when the following Resolutions were unanimously agreed to:

1. That the great and increasing Use of Sea-bathing is a strong Proof of the Advantages derived from that Remedy to such whose Circumstances admit of their resorting to the Coast.

2. That many valuable poor Sufferers, who might be relieved by the same Remedy, are deprived of it by the Expence attending a Residence at a Distance from their Families and Occupations.

3. That, notwithstanding the many Charitable Institutions already so well supported in Great Britain, it cannot be deemed an Intrusion on the Benevolence of the Publick to request their Attention to one for the sole Relief of such Objects of Compassion whose Diseases require Sea-bathing.

4. That the Vicinity of the Town of Margate appears well calculated for such an Institution, on account of the well-known Salubrity of that Part of the Coast, the ready and cheap Conveyance thither, and the probable Residence, during the Summer, of many of the Subscribers, who may inspect the Management of the House, and be satisfied concerning the proper Application of their Contributions.

5. That Ground, convenient for erecting such an Hospital, be forthwith purchased in the Names of Trustees for that Purpose; and that a Committee be appointed in London, to correspond with another at Margate, to carry the Design into Execution.

6. That Subscribers of One Guinea, or upwards, annually, shall be considered as Governors, and have a Power of nominating a Patient whenever there is a Vacancy; and that Subscribers of Twenty Guineas, or upwards, shall be Governors for Life.

7. That Subscriptions be received at the following Bankers; viz. Baron DIMSDALE and Co. Cornhill; DOWNE and Co. Bartholomew Lane; Sir R. C. GLYN and Co. Birchin Lane; GOSLING and Co. Fleet Street; Sir R. HERRIES and Co. St. James's Street; LADBROKE and Co. Bank Buildings; MILDRED and Co. White Hart Court, Gracechurch Street; PRESCOTTS and Co. Threadneedle Street; RANSOM and Co. Pall Mall; Sir J. SANDERSON and Co. Southwark; by Dr. LETTSOM, Basinghall Street, Treasurer; and by the Rev. JOHN PRIDDEN, 61, Salisbury Square, Fleet Street, Secretary.

*** Subscription Books are also left at the Public Rooms and Libraries at Margate, Ramsgate, and Broad-stairs.

read

23

Read a Letter from Samuel Whitbread, Esq; offering a Subscription of Fifty Guineas and further Support if necessary; also a Letter from a Lady inclosing a Ten-pound Note & desiring her Name to be concealed.

Resolved. That the Thanks of this Committee be given to Dr Lettsom for the Honour he has conferred upon them in calling them together upon such an important Occasion as introducing to the Public this benevolent and necessary Institution.

Resolved. That the Meeting of this Committee be adjourned to Monday July 11.th to meet at this House at six o'Clock.

It may be of interest to record the comments of Charles Lamb on the "superior advantages" of Margate. "We have been dull at Worthing one summer, duller at Brighton another, dullest at Eastbourne a third, and are at this moment doing dreary penance at — Hastings — and all because we were happy many years ago for a brief week at Margate." (Lamb, 1833)

In proposing the foundation of a Sea Bathing Infirmary, Lettsom envisaged a hospital where the patients could be housed in "solaria" (Raistrick, 1950), as well as having the treatment of being bathed in the sea at the same time. He appears to have had an instinctive intuition that much advantage would accrue if patients were to live in open-air shelters which thus afforded the added benefits of sea breezes and sunshine.

Lettsom, therefore, may truly be said to be the originator of open-air hospitals and, in consequence, this hospital was designed, from the first, with open-air arcades and verandahs.

On 5th July 1791 eight gentlemen went down to Margate and met Dr Anderson to inspect a site which was available at Westbrook and was the property of Isaac Rowe. It was in use as a brick-making yard. On the sale price of £300 for the site, with the vendor offering to defray the cost of conveyancing, a deposit of £5 was put down by Lettsom, Nichols and Pridden. The property extended to 450 feet by 140 feet with a right of way from the Margate to Dentdelion road.

Only six and a half weeks after the foundation of the Charity, and long before the hospital was built, a minute of 17th August 1791 reads: ". . . a letter from . . . Dr Kennedy by which he is informed His Royal Highness (the Prince of Wales) accepts the Patronage of the Margate Infirmary". The name of the Institution was changed, by Royal Permission, to that of "The Royal Sea Bathing Infirmary".

Turner's picture of Margate, reproduced on page six, is believed to have been engraved by Thomas Wallis, and is drawn from a spot almost exactly in front of the site of the hospital and was painted about 1832. It shows the tower of Holy Trinity Church which is not seen in the picture of 1830. This picture may have been drawn a year or two earlier because the church was built between 1827 and 1829, being finally completed in the latter year. The church was bombed in the 1939-1945 war and the tower later demolished as it was dangerous. Turner would have been seventeen in 1792, when the foundation stone of the hospital was laid and, indeed, first exhibited at the Royal Academy at the age of sixteen.

The Rev. John Pridden, one of Lettsom's most enthusiastic supporters, was an antiquary and amateur architect and designed a hospital which turned out to be too ambitious. A new design of simpler pattern was adopted but it retained the principle of "solaria".

MARGATE INFIRMARY.

Thursday the 21st instant being the day appointed for laying the first stone of the General Sea-bathing Infirmary, situated in West Sea-Bath Bay, near Margate, the Gentlemen of the London Committee in the morning joined the Gentlemen of the Margate Committee at the Town Hall where the friends to the institution were introduced to form a procession to the place above-mentioned; which immediately took place, the bells striking up, as the signal for it to commence, in the following order:

Two stands of colours,
A grand band of music,
Gentlemen two and two, &c. &c.

The spot of ground being prepared, the first stone was deposited in its place, the following inscription, which was engraved on a brass plate, was twice read by the Rev. Mr. Pridden, Secretary to the London Committee:

The first stone
Of an intended Infirmary,
For the purpose of Sea-Bathings,
To be supported by
VOLUNTARY BOUNTY,
Was laid on the 21st day of June, 1792,
In the presence of many rejoicing spectators,
By *John Coakley Lettsom*, M.D.

The plate being placed in a groove cut in the stone, was covered by a course of bricks, laid by Dr. Lettsom, who immediately addressed the concourse of people who attended in a pertinent speech of some length; which being ended, the Rev. Mr. Butler offered a solemn prayer that the Almighty might bless their pious, charitable undertaking. Lastly, at the ground, the company testified their warmest desires for its success, by joining in three times three cheers; when the procession re-commenced in the same order as before, and returned to Benson's hotel, where 26 gentlemen sat down to a most sumptuous entertainment.

COMMON PLEAS.

Serjeant Grant versus the Duke of York.

This was an action commenced by the plaintiff against his Royal Highness the Duke of York, as one of the Honourable Members of the Court Martial, lately held at Chatham, to recover a satisfaction in damages for the injury he had sustained by his late trial as a soldier.

Mr. Serjeant Adair, as Counsel for the Duke of York, lately obtained a rule for judgment as in case of a nonsuit, upon the usual ground, that the plaintiff had not proceeded to trial, pursuant to his notice.

This rule on Tuesday came on to be argued.

Mr. Martin, Attorney for Grant, informed the Court, that he had given briefs with fees to four Counsel, to plead the cause of the plaintiff, all which briefs had been refused, or returned. He said the reason of the delay in not proceeding to trial, arose from the necessity of taking time to confide what Counsel he should employ. He had every reason to believe, that he could adduce sufficient evidence to a Jury, that Grant was no soldier, and therefore entreated the Court to indulge him till the next Term to go to trial.

Mr. Serjeant Cockell said, that he felt himself called upon as one of the Counsel who had returned a brief sent to him on behalf of Grant, to say a few words. He was actuated by motives of delicacy in what he had done. He understood that Mr. Serjeant Marshall wished to have the sole management of the cause, as he had been alone entrusted with the late argument in support of the rule for the prohibition.

Mr. Serjeant Marshall denied that he had ever expressed a wish to have the sole management of the cause.

Mr. Serjeant Adair then contended, that by the rules of the Court he was entitled to have his rule made absolute, for, that there was no reasonable excuse for the plaintiff's not proceed-tary on the part of the defendant, he had a right to annex any condition to it he thought proper. As he had annexed a condition, it ought to have been proved that he was able to pay.

Lord Loughborough was of a different opinion; his Lordship conceived it lay with the defendant to prove his inability.

A new trial was granted.

To be peremptorily Sold,

Pursuant to a decree of the High Court of Chancery made in a cause, Sexagon, before John Wilmot, Esq. one of the Masters of the said Court, at his Chambers in Symons-inn, Chancery-lane, London, on Thursday the 19th day of July next, between the hours of Five and Six in the Afternoon, in two lots,

TWO FREEHOLD ESTATES of Adam Tunnock, deceased, situated at Bracon in the parish of Leek, in the county of Stafford

Printed particulars may be had gratis at the said Master's Chambers; of Mellis, Mills and Crosse, of Leek; and of Mr. Townsend, Staple-inn, London.

This Day was published,
In Four Volumes, Twelves,
The only complete Edition, ornamented with 12 elegant Engravings, price 10s. 6wed.

ARABIAN TALES: or, A Continuation of the ARABIAN NIGHTS ENTERTAINMENTS.

Consisting of stories related by the Sultana of the Indies, to divert her husband from the performance of a rash vow; exhibiting a most interesting view of the religion, laws, manners, customs, arts, and literature of the natives of the East; and affording a rich fund of the most pleasing amusement which fictitious writing can supply.

Newly Translated from the Original Arabic,
By DOM CHAVIS, a native Arab, and M. CARGOTTE, Member of the Academy of Dijon.

And Translated from the French into English,
By ROBERT HERON.

Printed for C. G. J. and J. Robinson, Paternoster-row...

The London Chronicle's report of the laying of the foundation stone.

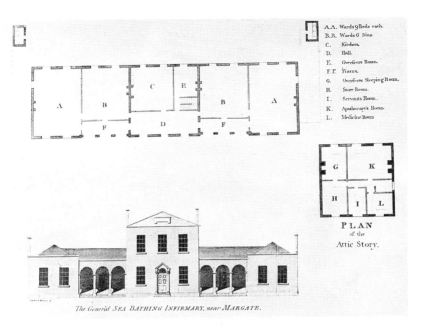

The original design of the Royal Sea Bathing Infirmary. West elevation.

The Hon. Philip Pusey accepted the Presidency of the Hospital on 1st May 1792 and in June the Committee met in Margate for the purpose of laying the foundation stone. Present were:

Francis Cobb, Vice-President, in the chair,

John Andrews, MD.
John Baker, Esq.
James Boswell, Esq.
  (The Laird of Auchinlech).
Mr John Silver, Surgeon.
Mr George Slater, Surgeon.
Francis Small, Gent.
John Smith, Esq.
Capt. John Stranack.
Thomas Taylor, Esq.

John Coakley Lettsom, MD.
Mr Deputy Nichols.
Rev. Weedon Butler.
William Norris, Esq.
Francis Cobb, Jr., Esq.
John Forbes, Gent.
William Hawes, MD.
Barnard Holbrook, Esq.
Capt. Stephen Hooper.
Rev. John Pridden.

The occasion was fully reported in the London Chronicle for 28-30th June 1792, page 662, and read as follows:

"MARGATE INFIRMARY".

"Thursday the 21st instant being the day appointed for laying the first stone of the General Sea Bathing Infirmary, situated in West Seabath (sic) (Seabrook) Bay, near Margate, the Gentlemen of the London Committee in the morning joined the Gentlemen of the Margate Committee at the Town Hall where friends of the Institution were introduced to form a procession to the place above-mentioned: which immediately took place, the bells striking up as the signal for it to commence, in the following order.

"Two stands of Colours.

"A grand band of music.

"Gentlemen two & two, &c., &c."

"The spot of ground being prepared, the stone was deposited in its place. The following inscription, which was engraved on a brass plate, was read twice by the Rev. Weedon Butler, Secretary to the London Committee:

"The first stone of an intended Infirmary for the purpose of Sea Bathing to be supported by VOLUNTARY BOUNTY was laid on the 21st day of June, 1792, in the presence of many rejoicing spectators, by John Coakley Lettsom, MD.

"The plate being placed in a groove cut in the stone, was covered by a course of bricks, laid by Dr Lettsom, who immediately addressed the concourse of people who attended in a pertinent speech of some length: which being ended, the Rev. Weedon Butler offered a solemn prayer that the Almighty might bless their pious, charitable undertaking.* Lastly, at the ground, the company testified their warmest desires for its success by joining in three times three cheers; when the procession re-commenced in the same order as before and returned to Benson's Hotel, when 46 gentlemen sat down to a most sumptuous entertainment." Amongst those participating in this ceremony was James Boswell, Dr Johnson's biographer, who was a member of the Committee.

However, all was not smooth sailing because of ". . . the uneasiness it (the projected hospital) created in the minds of the inhabitants (of Margate) and the animosity of others." It was therefore ". . . recommended to the Committee to consider a plan proposed to Dr Lettsom by some gentlemen, proprietors of land on the coast of Essex." This was on 18th July, only a month after laying the foundation stone at Margate!

The land was offered by Mr John Pratt and Thomas Holland, John Watts and Matthew Lowdown, Esquires, in the Parish of Prittlewell, Essex, ". . . to build an Infirmary convenient for thirty beds . . . without any expense to the Committee and to make it over to the Trustees appointed by the aforesaid Committee for the . . . term of 98 years."

---

* Rev. Weedon Butler was an ancestor of Mr R. Weedon Butler who was Senior Orthopaedic Surgeon at Addenbrook's Hospital, Cambridge, after World War II and who visited the Royal Sea Bathing Hospital with the Orthopaedic Section of the Royal Society of Medicine in 1966.

On 27th July 1792 Southend was visited by eight members of the Committee and the proposed site approved and on 9th August the offer of the Southend site was approved. However, Margate proposed a meeting on the 16th August to ". . . take the sense of the people respecting an Infirmary". So that decision was postponed.

During the following two months, Mr Holland was reported by Mr Pratt to be going to make some considerable contribution to the Committee. Exactly what this was is not known but may have related to the offer of free building at the Southend site. However, he did not appear to be able to make up his mind and was given to 24th October to do so! He then attended the Committee on that day and said that he "could not think of fulfilling the promise made by Mr Pratt on behalf of himself but the most he would agree to would be to furnish the Society with Bricks and Timber for the intended building at prime cost". Mr Pratt was "exonerated" from his promise and in the light of the offer it was agreed ". . . to relinquish all connection with Southend" as the Margate meeting showed ". . . it to be the general wish of the Town that the Institution of the Sea Bathing Infirmary should be established there".

The hospital was built at a cost of £1,766.10s.9d and furnished for £265.7s.7d (Abraham, l.c.). It was finally ready for the admission of thirty patients in the spring of 1796 (New Margate, Ramsgate and Broadstairs Guide, 1797). "The building is constructed in a very commodious manner . . . near the beach . . . and a bathing machine has been built for the patients' sole use" (Gentlemen's Magazine, 1796).

Each patient, recommended by a subscribing Governor, had first to be examined by a Medical Board, either at the Court Room of the London Workhouse or St George's Hospital and they were ferried down to Margate by the Margate "Hoy", the original fare being 4 shillings (Abraham, l.c.).

The journey down to Margate was not always comfortable and might take two days and nights. Hardwicke Lewis in "An Excursion to Margate in the month of June 1786", quoted by Walter Jerrold (1907), reported ". . . after tumbling and rumbling, tacking and re-tacking, we reached Margate" and he goes on to comment critically on the atmosphere in the cabin of the Hoy.

Whatever the salubrity of the climate of Margate, it must have been a pretty rowdy place in the eighteenth century, as the picture of the atmosphere in the Hoy suggests. Thomas Gray, "while staying at Denton in 1766, on a visit to Margate", designated it "a Bartholomew Fair by the sea-side" (Hillier, l.c. 72 & 295).

This was a reference to the market held annually on St Bartholomew's Day at Smithfield, London. This was the same day as the massacre of the Huguenots in France in 1572. Bartholomew Fair was instituted by Henry I in 1133 and became a great cloth market but gradually deteriorated until, in

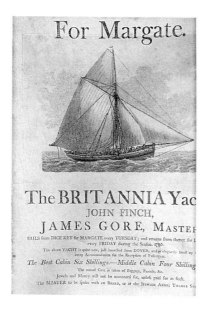

The Margate "Hoy"

The "atmosphere" in the hoy.

Fanciful drawing of the Royal Sea Bathing Infirmary at completion, 1796. From Cazin.

the eighteenth century, it had become the occasion of dissolution and riot, so much so that it was abolished in 1853.

Margate must have been a port of revelry and licence to have earned such descriptions and, indeed, it was said that "Prudes, in 1780, labelled Margate as 'devoted to gaiety and dissipation'" (Hillier, l.c. 74).

There are many gaps in the history of the Royal Sea Bathing Hospital for several reasons. In the first place, many of the records were lost when the London Headquarters of the Charity were bombed during the Second World War. Another reason is vividly illustrated by the second colour plate, showing how seriously damaged were many of the antique records and registers by a burst water-tank which was not discovered for a considerable time! In some of these, every trace of writing has been obliterated and in some of the rest rendered indecipherable or nearly so.

It was hoped, though never achieved until the National Health Service took over the hospital in 1948, that the Royal Sea Bathing Hospital should be a "free" hospital. But the patients had to pay five shillings a week, or 2/6d if twelve years of age or less, and their period of treatment was initially limited to six weeks, though some extension on medical grounds was permissible. An interesting commentary on this situation is that, in the monthly Medical Staff Meetings at the Kent & Canterbury Hospital, at least until 1967, the Consultant in charge of In-Patients who had exceeded the permitted six weeks was asked to justify the patient's retention!

Dr Jean André Venel

Venel's traction for scoliosis.

L'Hôpital Orthopédique de la Suisse Romande

Appendix 1
L'HOPITAL ORTHOPEDIQUE
DE LA SUISSE ROMANDE

In establishing the claim that the Royal Sea Bathing Hospital is the oldest orthopaedic hospital in the world one cannot overlook the story of *L'Hôpital Orthopédique de la Suisse Romande* at Lausanne. Jean-André Venel, 1740-1791, was the son of a *chirurgeon-perruquier* from Languedoc. He studied at Montpelier and then founded a "hospital" at Orbe, in the Canton of Vaud in Switzerland, in 1779 or 1780. It was of eight beds for the treatment of children, mostly suffering from scoliosis. The "hospital" was his own home, *L'Abbaye*. He must have obtained quite a considerable experience in this subject because he wrote a text-book on the treatment of scoliosis in 1788: *"Description de plusiers nouveaux Moyens Méchaniques propres à prévenir, borner* (to keep within bounds) *et même corriger, dans certains Cas, les Courbures latérales et la Tortion de l'Epine du Dos"*. Venel was primarily interested in training midwives to reduce the maternal mortality prevalent at that time. But, in 1776, a friend of his, a Pastor Nicati, asked him to treat his son's club foot. His success in this case led to the establishment of the "hospital" at Orbe.

Venel died of tuberculosis at the age of 51.

Venel's pupil was his nephew, Pierre-Frederic Jaccard (1768-1820), his first wife's brother's son. Venel's own son was only eleven at his father's death but his brother, Louis, was an apothecary and was responsible for continuing the interest in the subject of orthopaedics.

Jaccard was studying, at the age of 23, in Paris and was imprisoned, along with most other Swiss, in the terror of 1793. He was released through the good offices of the comedian, Collot d'Herbois, and returned to Orbe, taking over the work from his other uncle, Louis, who died in 1796.

In 1800 Jaccard married Jenny Boinod, of Aubonne and ultimately moved there. His sole surviving daughter, Danae, married Antoine-Paul Martin, one of her father's assistants (1794-1862) and they apparently kept some semblance of an orthopaedic programme going in their house, although no records of this exist and M. Martin was not registered under the law of 1st June 1810. Vaudoise legislation did not mention the word "orthopaedist" until 1850, over a hundred years after Nicholas André coined the term "Orthopaedia". There is, however, one undated letter in existence relating to a patient who was treated at Aubonne for club foot.

Martin died in 1862 when Henri, the eldest of his ten children, was studying at Geneva (no medical school had yet been established there). Henri Martin left and took over his father's work but apparently did not pass his examination in orthopaedics until 1868 and, it seems, never qualified as a doctor.

In 1873 Henri Martin moved to Lausanne and at that time usually had two or three patients resident in his home for the treatment of deformities. Throughout this time, the patients were all children and the orthopaedics was the orthopaedics of Nicholas André. From the first, or at least from very early on, the children's parents might be admitted during the child's treatment.

Within about three years of moving to Lausanne, a union was arranged with the children's hospital and the result was called *L'Hospice orthopédique de la Suisse Romande*. The "Romande" signifying, of course, that patients were accepted from all over French-speaking Switzerland and not just from the Canton of Vaud.

On 22nd September 1876 a committee was formed and Henri Martin was the "Director". The hospital received official recognition by the Council of State on 8th December 1876 and celebrated its centenary in 1976. Three beds were allotted for orthopaedics. Separation of the Orthopaedic Department came three or four years later following the advice of Dr Joel, physician to the Children's Hospital.

"Nous sommes assaillis de présentes demandes pour les enfants affligés de ces déformations qui present douloureusement sur toute l'existence, et l'Hospice d'Enfance, en leur consécrant trois lits, a fait la part qu'il pouvait à ces misères, mais ce chiffre est absolument insuffisant, et d'autre part ces enfants, vivant dans un milieu d'hôpital, en subissent trop souvent les influences. Ils ont eu precédement la colquelouche, ils ont souffert des epidémies de stomatite aphtheuse qui nous visitent de temps en temps, et récemment encore ils ont payés leur tribute à une grave épidémie d'ophthalmies catarrhales et purulentes qui a envahi nos salles.

"A mon avis, un institût orthopédique doit être entièrement distinct d'un hôpital . . ."

"We are assailed by the current demands on behalf of the children afflicted with these deformities which affect their whole lives with pain and disability and the Children's Hospital, in allocating three beds for them, has done what it could for the poor things, but this provision is totally inadequate. In addition, these children, living in the mileau of a hospital, have too often been subjected to its effects. Not long ago, they contracted whooping cough, they have suffered from epidemics of aphthous stomatitis which develops here from time to time, and yet again recently, they have paid their tribute to a serious epidemic of catarrhal and purulent ophthalmia which invaded our wards.

"My advice is that an orthopaedic hospital should be entirely separate from a hospital."

Amongst the staff at that time was Dr Edouard Martin-Du Pan who served from 1877 to 1927 and was followed by his son Charles (1878-1948) who also became renowned as an orthopaedic surgeon.

In 1878 the hospital moved into the Villa Chantilly, where it had twelve beds at its disposal.

In 1899 Dr Placide Nicod became assistant at the age of 23, serving as such until 1906, when he became chief of the hospital and filled this position until 1947. He was followed by Dr Jean-Charles Scholder until 1953 and then by Dr Louis Nicod who remains the present Professor of Orthopaedics in the Faculty of Medicine in the University of Lausanne. He is the son of Dr Placide Nicod.

(Reference: Hugli, L. and Nicod, L. 1976. *Centième Anniversaire de l'Hôpital Orthopédique de la Suisse Romande. Lausanne, Les Presses Centrales de Lausanne.* Permission to quote extensively from this history has been given by the Administrative Director of the hospital.) We are most indebted to Dr Louis Nicod who has kindly presented us with a copy of the history.

From this history, it would seem that orthopaedics were being carried out rather sporadically in private homes, rather than in a hospital, prior to the formation of *L'Hôpital Orthopédique de la Suisse Romande.* The Orthopaedics resembled more the practice of the Welsh Bone-Setters than the planned and medically guided history of the Royal Sea Bathing Hospital. *L'Hôpital Orthopédique de la Suisse Romande* frankly celebrated its *centenary* in 1976, thus making no pretensions of being more than one hundred years old at that time.

Appendix 2
JOHN COAKLEY LETTSOM, 22.11.1744-1.11.1815
MD, LL.B, FRS, FAS, FLS, FRCP (Edinburgh)

Founder of the Medical Society of London and through it, of the Royal Society of Medicine.
Founder of the Royal Sea Bathing Hospital.
Joint founder of the Royal Humane Society.
Supporter of Dr Wraugham, founder of a Northern Sea Bathing Infirmary at Scarborough.
Prison Reformer.
Gemmologist and Geologist.
Botanist.
Supporter of Jenner.
Introducer of the Mangel-Wurzel into Britain.
Promoter of Tea Drinking.
Hon. Member, Colchester Medical Society.
Hon. Member, Royal Medical Society of Edinburgh, 1788.

Fellow of the American Academy of Arts and Sciences.
Hon. Member, Medical Society of New York, 1789.
Hon. Member, Medical Society of New Haven.
Hon. Member, Agricultural Society of Amsterdam.
Hon. Member, Bath Agricultural Society.
Member, The Academy of Arts and Sciences, Montpelier, 1790.
William Fothergill Gold Medallist, Medical Society of London, 1791.
Hon. Member, Medical Society of Montpelier.
Member, University of Cambridge, Massachusetts.
D.LL. University of Cambridge, Massachusetts.
Hon. Member, Massachusetts Humane Society.
Corresponding Member, Medical Society of Bristol.
Hon. Member, Medical Society of Massachusetts, 1792.
Member, Pennsylvanian Society for Promoting the Abolition of Slavery.
Member, Massachusetts Historical Society.
Corresponding Member, Royal Academy of Sciences, Montpelier.
Hon. Member, Literary & Philosophical Society of Newcastle, 1793.
Hon. Member, Massachusetts Agricultural Society.
Corresponding Member, Historical Society of Boston.
Hon. Member and Conservator, the Hospital of New York, 1798.
Hon. Member, The Humane Society of Pennsylvania, 1801.
Associate of the College of Physicians, 1802.
Physician to the Camberwell Voluntary Infirmary, 1803.
Corresponding Member, Medical Lyceum of Philadelphia, 1808.
Hon. Member and later President, Philosophical Society of London, 1812.
Hon. Member, New York Historical Society, 1813.
Hon. Member, Horticultural Society of Edinburgh.
Hon. Member, Linnean Society of New England, 1815.
(Pettigrew, l.c.)

There is a famous doggerel verse, no doubt quite wrongly attributed to Lettsom, which runs approximately as follows:

> "If any sick they bring to me
> I physics, bleeds and sweats 'em.
> If after that they choose to die,
> What's that to me? I Lettsom."

(There are several versions of this verse, the one reproduced here is the one most enjoyed by the author!)

Chapter 2
THE FIRST PATIENTS

The first patients to be admitted to the Royal Sea Bathing Hospital were admitted in May 1796. During the summer of this year a total of sixteen patients came in and every year the numbers increased until, in 1800, the admissions reached eighty-six. Although the bed strength was only thirty, a stay of six weeks would allow several patients to use the same bed seriatim. For many years the hospital was only open in the summer months. This seems hardly surprising when it is remembered that a major part of the patients' treatment was being bathed in the sea at Margate! The "season" ended at the end of October or early in November.

Dr Anderson, who was a Margate Medical Practitioner and had been instrumental in helping Lettsom to find the site for the hospital, acted as the hospital's first Visiting Medical Officer and in 1799 a Mrs Nash was appointed Matron and Zachariah Cozens as Hospital Steward. The local Treasurer was Ronald Symes and James Taddy was the London Treasurer.

The following was the composition of the staff of the Royal Sea Bathing Infirmary in 1801.

Consulting Physicians
Sir Walter Farquhar, Bt. MD.
Maxwell Garthshore, MD.
James Sims, MD.

Consulting Surgeons
Thomas Keate, Esq.
William Blizard, Esq.
William Norris, Esq.

Physicians in Ordinary
Algernon Frampton, MD.
Samuel Holland, MD.

Surgeons
Mr George Slater.
Mr John Silver.
Mr Robert Edward Hunter.
Mr Daniel Jarvis.
Mr George Slater, Jun.
Mr Christopher Mayhew.
Mr William Neave Daniel.
Mr Samuel Frome.

It will be seen that the distinction between Doctor (MD), the physician and Mr (no apparent qualification), the surgeon, was already appearing and thus explains the unique nomenclature of "Doctor" and "Mister" which still persists in Britain.

There are many interesting facets in the records which throw light on the circumstances of those days. For instance, the cost of "bread for poultices" from 10th May to 7th October was £2.15s.8d and Mary Brockman submitted her bill for bathing the patients thirty-one times between 10th September and 7th November for £2.6s.6d. It seems that Zachariah Brazier

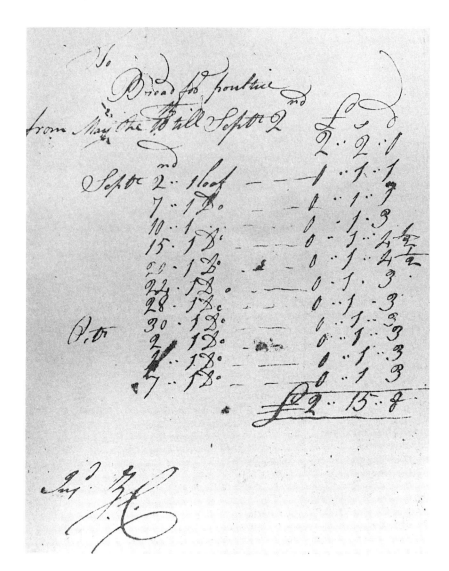

		£	s	d
To Bread for poultice from May the 10 till Septr 2		2	2	1
Septr 2 · 1 loaf		1	1	1
7 · 1 Do		0	1	1
10 · 1 Do		0	1	3
15 · 1 Do		0	1	4½
20 · 1 Do		0	1	4½
23 · 1 Do		0	1	3
28 · 1 Do		0	1	3
30 · 1 Do		0	1	3
Octr 2 · 1 Do		0	1	3
4 · 1 Do		1	1	3
7 · 1 Do		0	1	3
	£	2	15	8

Bread for poultices

Fly leaf of the Register for 1801. Numbers of patients admitted since the opening in 1796.

(sic) approved payment on 2nd December of that year. Reference to the first colour plate in chapter one may give some idea of what an arduous task was Mary Brockman's. She may well be thought of as one of the two rather large ladies who are "bathing a patient" from one of Beale's bathing machines and obviously taking pains to do so as kindly as possible. The steward's emolument for the year, paid on 18th July 1800, was twenty-five guineas (£26.5s.0d).

It was the custom of the Board of Governors to visit the hospital in the early autumn and then dine together afterwards. One account was for a dinner at the Royal Hotel for £9.6s.6d on the "1st/2nd" September. (They seem to have made a "proper meal" of it.) A little later a description will be given of Lettsom's annual holiday and there may be a connection between the two.

As well as an Honorary Visiting Surgeon, there was always a Resident Surgeon from the first but we could find no record of early occupants of the post.

One of the earliest Hospital Registers starts in 1801 when, on 6th May, the first patient admitted that year was Sarah Smith, suffering from "scrofula". Her age is not given, but no child under six was allowed to be admitted. She was recommended by G. Shaley. Every patient had to be recommended by a Governor and examined medically by one of the panel of doctors in London before being sent down to Margate. She had been examined by William Norris, who was always very active in this respect, and

Sea Bathing Infirmary Margate 18..

Mary Brockman for Bathing

the Patients 31 Times from September
the 10 to November the 7   £   s   d

Please to ...... Brazier   2 : 6 : 6
pay this   Steward
                  2 Dec. 18..

Mary Brockman

Mary Brockman's bill

No.	Admitted.	NAMES.	Complaints.	Recommended by	Examined by	Discharged.	No. of Times bathed.
1	May 6th	Sarah Smith	Scrophula	G. Tetsley	Wm Norris	...	72
2	— —	Dorothy Gass	Sore Leg	Lady Hone	Wm Blizard	July 5	22
3	— —	Harriot Compton		Jos Hannan	Wm Norris	July	25
4	— 7th	Wm Wells		Tho. Pickford	Wm Norris	June 16	14
5	— 13th	James Brown		P. Elliot	Wm Norris	Aug	37
6	— —	John Welch		J. Chitver	Wm Vaughan		38
7	— —	Daniel Man		Sarah Page	J. Sims	Sept 1	36

First entry: Sarah Smith, scrofula. Examined by William Norris. Dorothy Gass, sore leg. Examined by William Blizard.

40

she was ultimately discharged on 31st October 1801 with the comment that she had been "much benefitted". Against the record of her discharge is the information that she had been bathed seventy-two times. This means that she must have been bathed daily, even, possibly, sometimes on Sundays. However, Mary Brockman only charged for working thirty-one times over a period of sixty days. She may have had a colleague to share the work. The second patient, Dorothy Gass, had been examined by William Blizard who, as Sir William, became Master of the Royal College of Surgeons of London (its name at the time) in 1814.

Every patient had, from the outset, a quart of table beer or porter daily and the children a pint of table beer. The menus invariably included half a pound of beef or mutton for every patient every day for lunch (Lettsom, 1801). Some further examples of the dietary are discussed below.

As mentioned, the patients came down from London by the "Margate Hoy", a sailing vessel which, it is believed, was not unlike the Thames barges of recent history. They sailed from London Bridge to Margate but the length of the journey was not always constant! Charles Lamb gives a fascinating eyewitness account of the journey down to Margate when one of the passengers was a boy coming for admission to the hospital.

"The Old Margate Hoy"

". . . all this time, sat upon the edge of the deck quite a different character. It was a lad, apparently very poor, very infirm and very patient. His eye was ever on the sea, with a smile . . . He was as one, being with us, but not of us. He heard the bell of dinner ring without stirring; and when some of us pulled out our private stores — our cold meats and our salads — he produced none, and seemed to want none. Only a solitary biscuit had he laid in, provision for the one or two days and nights, to which these vessels were oftentimes obliged to prolong their voyage. Upon a nearer acquaintance with him, which he seemed neither to court nor decline, we learned that he was going to Margate with the hope of being admitted into the Infirmary there for Sea-Bathing. His disease was scrofula, which appeared to have eaten all over him. He expressed great hopes of a cure, and when we asked him, whether he had any friends where he was going, he replied he had no friends." (Lamb, 1833)

(This was one of Charles Lamb's "last essays" and, as such, was written between 1832 and his death in 1837. He states in it that he was fifteen at the time of this voyage, which would have dated the episode at 1790, before the hospital was founded. His memory must have been a little vague for he must have been at least twenty-one because the first patient to the hospital was not admitted until 1796.)

About this time a Miss Ann Osborn was a patient over a period of about seven years, although the treatment would have been interrupted by the closure of the hospital in the winter months. She survived what must have been a considerable infection to become the Assistant Matron in 1815.

Carlton House
March 1ST 1812.

The Prince Regent hereby gives His
Vote in favour of Mr R. W. Brown on the
Re-election of a Resident Surgeon to the Margate
Sea-Bathing Infirmary, vacant by the death
of Mr Eyles.

In His Royal Highness the
His Command.
J. McMahon
Secretary.

To Dr Lettsom
a Governor &c.

HRH the Prince Regent's letter.

42

It may be appropriate here to discuss the description "scrofula". Originally known as "The King's Evil", it was used to describe swelling of the glands of the neck and was later applied to swelling of glands generally. As these swellings were usually in the flexures of joints, the cause of the glandular enlargement was often disease in the joints. And the swellings may not even always have been of the glands but may have been cold abscesses, as such infections would often have been tuberculous in nature. A great many of the admissions were designated Disease of Hip, Knee or Spine, which is further confirmation that "scrofula" was not limited to the glands of the neck. In this way, the hospital came to have as its major responsibility the treatment of bone and joint tuberculosis, ever a discipline of orthopaedics.

Erasmus Wilson was born in 1809. He was to become the greatest benefactor of the hospital and subsequently became President of the Royal College of Surgeons of England.

In 1811 the Resident Surgeon at the Royal Sea Bathing Hospital was a Mr Eyles. Sadly, however, he died the following year. No doubt, so long as the infective nature of tuberculosis was unknown and prophylactic measures therefore lacking, many of the staff of the hospital must have contracted the disease and many must have died in harness. Mr Eyles was followed by Dr R.W. Brown. As an indication of the personal involvement of the Prince of Wales, now Prince Regent, in the affairs of the hospital as its Patron, a letter from him speaks for itself. Dated at Carlton House, March 11th 1812, it gives the Prince's vote for the election of a Resident Surgeon to fill the post vacant as a result of Dr Eyles' death. The following is the full text of the letter:

"Carlton House, March 11th, 1812.
The Prince Regent hereby gives his vote in favour of Mr R.W. Brown in the election of a Resident Surgeon to the Margate Sea Bathing Infirmary, vacant by the death of Mr Eyles.
For His Royal Highness and by His command,
J. McMahon, Secretary.
To Dr Lettsom, a Governor, &c."

At the head of the organisation for handling the affairs of the Royal Sea Bathing Hospital was the Patron. The Prince of Wales had accepted this appointment within six weeks of the founding of the hospital, as mentioned in the previous chapter. He subsequently became King George IV and from that time on was followed by every Monarch in turn as Patron of the hospital, with the exception of King Edward VIII (see below).

The detailed organisation of the affairs of the Royal Sea Bathing Hospital was the responsibility of a Court of Directors in London, normally under the Chairmanship of a President. It was advised by the London Medical Board which consisted of senior medical men in various spheres of

43

GENERAL
Sea-Bathing Infirmary.

A

BALL,

TO

AID THE FUNDS OF THIS INSTITUTION,

WILL TAKE PLACE

ON MONDAY,

The 25th of August, 1817,

At the Royal Hotel,

MARGATE.

The Patronage of the Nobility and Gentry on the above occasion, is respectfully entreated by the Margate Committee of the Charity.

PATRONESSES.

Countess DELAWARRE	Mrs. DEVAYNES
Lady ELIZABETH DORMER	Mrs. FORSYTH
Honourable Mrs. GARDNER	Mrs. GREY
Lady DERING	Mrs. GODFREY
Lady LAKE	Mrs. POWELL
Lady FRASER	Mrs. TADDY
Lady ANSON	Mrs. WARRE
The Lady MAYORESS	

STEWARDS.

Right Hon. Earl DELAWARRE	SAMUEL BROOKE, Esq.
Right Hon. Lord BARNARD	BENJAMIN COCK, Esq.
Right Hon. the LORD MAYOR of	WILLIAM DEVAYNES, Esq.
LONDON, M.P., V.P.	JAMES DYSON Esq.
Hon. Captain GARDNER	STEPHEN ELLIS, Esq.
Sir JAMES LAKE, Bart.	JOHN FRIEND, Esq.
Sir WILLIAM FRASER, Bart.	J. P. POWELL, Esq.
Maj.-Gen. Sir GEORGE ANSON, K.C.B.	JAMES TADDY, Esq. V.P.
Dr. BROWN, M.D.	T. J. TAYLER. Esq.
Dr. GREY, M.D.	THOMAS WARRE, Esq. V.P.

TICKETS, 7s. each, to be had at the Libraries, in Margate, Ramsgate, and Broadstairs.

A ball in aid of the Sea Bathing Infirmary in 1817. (KCL)

Advertisement for a Ball in aid of the hospital.

44

activity though it was probably too early to call them specialists. Certainly there was a distinction between physicians and surgeons but there the difference ceased. Throughout the history of the hospital until 1948 the Medical Board in London continued to comprise medical men of the highest reputation.

As a hospital supported by "voluntary bounty", there was the recurrent problem of raising sufficient finance to keep it adequately supplied with its day-to-day needs. Various methods were used to attract funds, one of which was popular at the time and which continued to be a recognised fund-raising exercise throughout the nineteenth century and, indeed, even up to the present time. This was in the form of a Charity Ball and the illustration shows how the use of titled patrons was expected to boost the attendance of the public as long ago as 1817! As might be expected in those days, it was not the general public that were invited to attend but the "nobility and gentry"!

It will be observed that some of the names carry the letters "V.P." after them. These were Vice-Presidents of the Charity. Their duties were not laid down but it seems that lending their names to an occasion such as this was one of them. Presumably one of them would act as Chairman of a meeting when the Hospital President was unable to attend.

While Lettsom was elected as the first Treasurer of the hospital, he must have handed the position on very shortly as James Taddy was the noted Treasurer at the turn of the century. Upon his shoulders lay the whole responsibility for the stability of the financial structure and it is apparent that he not only achieved great success in this sphere but became a very revered person himself. A fine portrait of him is seen in the colour illustrations.

One of the methods of fund-raising was the encouragement of people to become Governors. Anyone who made a donation of ten pounds to the charity became a Governor and had the privilege of nominating a patient for admission. It seems that such a nomination could only be made once a year and some Governors were limited to the number of years they could hold the privilege. Some appear to have held it longer, but they may, perhaps, have paid more for the honour.

While the general organisation was run from London, there was a Margate Local Management Committee whose duty was to handle the day-to-day affairs of the hospital, that is to say, anything that lay outside the normal activities of the Resident Surgeon, Matron and Hospital Steward.

Once a year, usually towards the end of August or early in September, the Directors, Physicians and Surgeons, Governors and other well-wishers from London paid a visit to the Royal Sea Bathing Hospital at Margate. This was also the occasion of Lettsom's only annual holiday and it will be seen that the description "holiday" is really a distinct euphemism! We have some information on the visit of 1813:

Lettsom left in the packet from Billingsgate at four o'clock on the Saturday afternoon and, sailing all night down the Thames Estuary and the never reliable North Sea, arrived at Margate on that occasion on the Sunday morning.

He arrived in time to hear the Rev. David Garrow, son of Sir William Garrow, the Attorney General, preach the annual sermon on behalf of the hospital at the New Chapel, Ramsgate. After lunch, Lettsom saw private patients in Ramsgate, Broadstairs and Margate and then dined and spent the night at Pegwell with Sir William Garrow. (New Margate, Ramsgate and Broadstairs Guide, 1816.)

All the pulpits in Thanet that weekend were devoted to the Royal Sea Bathing Hospital, amongst the preachers being the Rev. Charles Hughes and the Rev. Henry Ingley, DD, and some £245.0s.5d was collected in five churches (Gen. Sea Bathing Minutes, 1813-1837). Additional donations brought the total up to £454.8s.11d that weekend. Considerable subscribers included some local names which are still famous locally today, such as Lord Sondes who contributed ten guineas, Lady Burton donated £10 and Wyndham Knatchbull £25.

On the Monday morning, Lettsom and William Norris, Consulting Surgeon to the Royal Sea Bathing Hospital and Surgeon to the Charterhouse and General Dispensary in Aldersgate Street, went to the Hospital and examined every patient. In the late afternoon they made a report to the Annual General Meeting of the Governors. They describe how they had found ". . . 120 patients in the General Sea Bathing Infirmary, the greater part of whom were in a rapidly improving state of health" (Minutes 30.8.1813). There were also, at the time, some eighty local residents from the Isle of Thanet who were receiving ". . . the benefits of sea bathing and medicine" as out patients. Prayers were said daily and ". . . such patients as were able attended Divine Worship on Sundays".

Amongst the patients who were singled out as having made striking progress were Mary Allen, Elizabeth Fryer, Agnes Service, Ann Cook, John Marston, Isabella Robson, Ann Mitchell and Elizabeth Frome.

The Annual General Meeting expressed its appreciation of the services of Rev. Hughes and Rev. Ingley and also of the efforts of the ladies who had helped with the collections, namely, Rt. Hon. Countess Mamey, Rt. Hon. Lady George Seymour, Rt. Hon. Lady Catherine Bricknell, Mrs Neve, Mrs Althorpe, Mrs Forsyth (of Pierremont House, Broadstairs, wife of Thomas Forsyth) and Miss Boodle. They were all made Lady Patronesses.

Present also at the AGM were Sir Christopher Pegge, the Hon. George Watson, Rev. David Garrow, the Treasurer, Michael Gibbs, Esq., ". . . and there were elected to the Margate Committee for the following year: Francis Cobb; Francis William Cobb; the Vicar of St John's, Margate, Rev. Frederick Bayly and local doctors and surgeons: Dr Thomas Brown, Dr Thomas Grey and George Slater. Rev. George Townshend reported receipts from Rev. Charles Townley, LL.D., Rev. Henry Townley and Rev. Charles Mayhew."

That evening, the Directors, Governors and Patrons all dined with their visitors and guests and three other Vice-Presidents: Sir Horace Mann, Bt., James Taddy (the London Treasurer) and Francis Cobb. It may have been such a dinner for which the account mentioned earlier was paid.

After the dinner, Lettsom took the post chaise from Margate at 7 o'clock (he clearly did not participate in a occasion which ran on into the following day!) and arrived in London at 10 o'clock the next morning ready to resume his practice. Such was his annual "holiday"!

The two Cobbs mentioned above were members of the Cobb family who were brewers in Margate and their firm persisted into the 1960s. It was an extremely influential family in the town:

Francis Cobb	1726-1802
Francis Cobb	1759-1831
Francis William Cobb	1787-1871

They held the Deputy Mayoralty of Margate for very many years under the Mayor of Dover, of which "Cinque Port" Margate was, and still is, a "Limb".

They built a new brewery, completed on 6th July 1808, for £60,000 (Cobb, 1835, and Licensed Victuallers' Gazette, 1875).

One of the Cobb family was a doctor and was Visiting Surgeon to the charity in 1823 and another Dr Cobb was a General Practitioner and Surgeon to the Victoria Hospital, Dover, before, during and after the war of 1939-45.

This chapter ends with the death of John Coakley Lettsom, founder of the Royal Sea Bathing Hospital and author of so many philanthropic activities as to make him one of the great benefactors of the eighteenth century. In such high esteem was Lettsom held that Thomas Joseph Pettigrew wrote a three volume memoir and collection of Lettsom's letters which he published as early as 1817. The three volumes were presented to the hospital on 20th December 1900 by Mrs Joseph Elliot Edlmann, great-grand-daughter of John Coakley Lettsom.

Pettigrew's "Life of Lettsom" started with a list of subscribers to the charity and amongst these were S.T. Coleridge, Edward Jenner and two Norfolk Stylemans.

The hospital in 1816. Note the windmill.

The hospital in 1816. No windmill.

48

Chapter 3
EARLY DAYS

Mrs Nash, who had served as Matron from 1799, died in 1815 and was followed by Mary Foster. Miss Osborn, as mentioned earlier, became Assistant Matron. It seems that Mr Nash had been appointed as Hospital Steward in the place of Zachariah Cozens but, in 1815, he was discharged from the post and Zachariah Cozens returned for a short time to fill the vacancy until a successor was appointed, which proved to be J. Matthews. We shall hear more of Mr Matthews shortly.

The year after Lettsom died, a new wing was completed. It brought the bed-strength up to ninety and extended towards Margate from the most southerly extremity of the hospital. Two illustrations, both dating from 1816, show a slightly different aspect of the result. One shows a small, four-sweep windmill close to the end of the new extension but it has disappeared in the other illustration. As these illustrations were, of course, drawings and not photographs, the windmill may represent a trace of "artist's licence"! Alternatively, it may have been pulled down that year although it does not appear in any of the earlier pictures.

Amongst the many enlargements of the hospital which were undertaken from time to time, and which started in 1816, a considerable extension was built, according to Newman (1969) in 1820 or thereabouts. This was the erection of the present front, "a Grecian Block, nine bays wide, two-storeyed, with a monumental Doric four-columned portico". It is always averred locally that the Doric columns came from Holland House in Kingsgate on the North Foreland. This was said to be one of Lord Holland's "Follies", for which he was famous. It is not known whether this was built by the celebrated architect Henry Holland (20.6.1745-17.6.1806) who also designed the original Regent's Pavilion at Brighton for the then Prince of Wales. The Regent's Pavilion, was, of course, altered much later by Nash.

The columns are a spectacular feature of the hospital entrance and in the early post Second World War years, were overgrown with ivy (see frontispiece). This may not have been good for the stonework and so was all removed in 1962 and the facade cleaned up for the meeting of the British Orthopaedic Association at Margate in April of that year.

The inscription carved over the hospital entrance reads: "The Royal Sea Bathing Hospital. Founded 1791". This suggests that this inscription is of much later date because the hospital was known as the Royal Sea Bathing Infirmary at least until the end of the nineteenth century.

1821

No.	Admitted.	No. of Ticket.	Name of Patient.	Age.	Residence.	Recommended by
1	May 14.	102	Thomas Collis	9	Hammersmith	Harry Stoe
2	— 14.	3	Anthony Breman	11	Vernon Place Bloomsbury Sqᵉ	John Blades
3	— 14.	41	John Goulet	19	31 Primrose St Bishopgate	John Pugh
4	— 14.	141	Lucy Lindsey	9	5 Mansfield Place Kentish Town	William Randall
5	— 14.	25	Sarah Matthews	6	60 Skinner St Bishopgate	Henry Salkeld
6	— 14	120	Edward Stanley	0	34 Grove Street Camden Town	John Blades
7	— 14	90	John T. How —	12		Joseph Fry
8	— 14.	54	George Brantz	5	51 Leather Lane	Willᵐ Wigram
9	— 14.	50	James Edwards	5	71 Moffatt Terrace City Road	James Montague

First entry: Thomas Collis, scrofula.

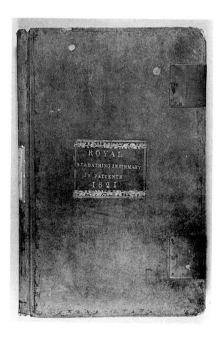

Patient register for 1821.

Examined by	Complaint	Discharged	Certificate and Remarks
M.B.	Scrofula	July 23	Much Benefit
M.B	Diseased Spine	Oct. 1.	Great Benefit
M.B.	Do. Right Knee	July 31.	A. Cure
M.B.	Do. Knee	July 10	Very Great Benefit
M.B.	Do. Spine & Hip	June 12.	No Benefit
M.B.	Do. Right Hip	Oct. 29	Great benefit
M.B.	Do. Hip & Knee	July 24.	Great Benefit
M.B.	Scrofula	Oct. 29.	Great benefit
M.B.	Diseased Right Knee	Oct. 29	Great benefit

At this time, a Caretaker for the winter was appointed, a Mr Taylor, which was obviously a necessary precaution as the hospital would be empty from early November until the beginning of May and this was to continue to be the case for another thirty-five years. William Oliver Chalk was appointed as Resident Surgeon in 1820 and will appear more than once in these pages, as he served for twenty-five years.

The further additions to the hospital seem to have raised the bed strength very considerably. Figures, however, seem to vary widely and later ones hardly confirm that the numbers as early as the third decade of the century could have been no less than the remarkable figure of 243. Certainly there must have been more than the ninety beds available at the second week of May 1821, when sixty-seven adults and thirty-two children were admitted. The first patient appearing in the Patients' Register for 1821 was Thomas Collis, aged nine, who was admitted on 14th May from Hammersmith. He was discharged on 23rd July following treatment for "scrofula" with the comment: "Much Benefit".

The undoubted orthopaedic nature of the work, even at this early stage, can be seen in the diagnoses of nine of the next nineteen admissions, which indicated that the spine, hip, knee and "arm" were the site of the disease. It is further to be observed that the term "scrofula" was not, even then, limited to tuberculosis of the glands of the neck, when one of the diagnoses reads: "Scrofulous Hip and Arm".

51

May	Bread.	Flour.	Beef.	Mutton.	Butter.	Cheese.	Rice.	Oatmeal.	Salt.	Pepper.	
	lbs oz	Galls			lbs	lbs	lbs	Gall	lbs	lb	
Monday - 14th	78.3	4		40	17	15	4	3	14	1/4	
Tuesday - 15th	52.2		40								
Wednesday 16th	52.2			87							
Thursday - 17th	78.3			44							
Friday 18th	78.3		24								
Saturday - 19th	104.4		172								
Sunday - 20											
WEEK First	443.1	4	176	173	17	15	4	3	14	1/4	
Monday - 21	104.4		53		25	27½	6	6			
Tuesday - 22	104.4	6		47							
Wednesday 23	104.4		114								
Thursday - 24	104.4										

Entry in Provisions Book, 1821.

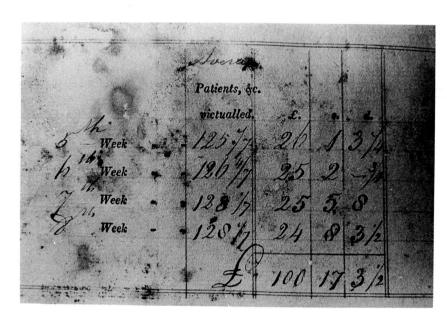

	Patients, &c. victualled.	£.	s.	d.
5th Week	125 7/	26	1	3½
6th Week	126 4/	25	2	3/
7th Week	128 /7	25	5	8
8th Week	128 /7	24	8	3½
£		100	17	3½

Cost of feeding patients, 1821.

The original pewter bread plates.

The treatment of these poor patients, many of whom were distinctly undernourished, paid special attention to their diets. The staff also shared in the high standard of catering which must have been of great importance in helping them resist the infection to which they were continuously exposed.

The Provisions Book for 1821 makes most interesting reading. It will be seen that, for ninety-nine patients and eleven staff, the following was provided for the week's rations:

Bread	443 lbs	Mustard	¼ lb
Flour	4 gallons	Pepper	¼ lb
Beef	176 lbs	Vinegar	2 quarts
Mutton	173 lbs	Tea	½ lb
Butter	17 lbs	Currants	4 lbs
Cheese	13 lbs	Milk	90.1 quarts
Rice	4 lbs	Beer	227 gallons
Oatmeal	3 gallons	Wine	12 bottles
Salt	14 lbs		

(Glossary: 4 quarts = 1 gallon. 1 gallon = approximately 4½ litres. 1 lb (pound) = 454g.)

Other supplies at subsequent dates included potatoes, bacon, pearl barley, sago, arrowroot, treacle and honey. Each patient had more than three pounds of red meat a week and over half a pound of bread a day. Each had two gallons of beer a week (1.3 litres a day) but only a tenth of that amount of milk! The amounts are the more remarkable when it is remembered that at least a third of the patients were children. It certainly looks as if the concept of "building up a patient's resistance" was adequately taken care of.

53

In 1821 the cost of feeding a patient for a week was about four shillings (RSBHA 358).

The original pewter bread plates are shown in the illustrations and these were used to take the bread round to the patients. They are engraved "Margate Infry" on the rim.

By the time the house closed on 3rd November 1821, a total of 150 patients had been treated. Eighty-nine were listed as "cured" or "greatly benefitted", thirteen "improved", "no significant improvement" in twenty-two and one died. As is still liable to happen today, one patient was discharged for "misconduct"!

The majority of patients were in the first three decades of life, an incidence comparable with that of the first half of the twentieth century. Ten patients were between thirty and thirty-six and one each aged forty, forty-five and fifty-four. The diagnoses for that year were as follows:

Scrofula	57
Spine	8
Hip	17
Knee	12
Ancle	5
Leg	9
Foot	5
Other	11

In addition, there were four "scorbutic" cases and other assorted diagnoses.

In 1823 a Mrs Icken asked Dr Cobb, then the Honorary Visiting Surgeon, to present a patient:

"Mrs Icken, Dover, August 24th, 25th and 26th 1823.

"Mrs Icken presents her compliments to Mr Cobb and should be extremely obliged to him to put her in a way to get a poor motherless child, suffering from scrofula in her hip joint, admitted into the Royal Sea Bathing Infirmary. The medical Gentlemen of the Canterbury Hospital have declared that the child's health is better and that nothing can benefit her, but sea air and water, with good food which cannot be procured for her at home, therefore having heard much of the valuable Margate Institution and knowing the benevolence of Mr Cobb's character Mrs Icken has taken the liberty to apply to him on behalf of this little sufferer.

"Mrs Icken hopes Mrs Styleman was well when Mr C. heard from her and will be obliged by his presenting her remembrances when he writes to her.

Castle Hill, Dover, Sunday 24th August."

The draft of Mr Cobb's reply was as follows:

"Margate, 26th August 1823.

"Mr Cobb has pleasure to hand to Mrs Icken the accompanying ticket for admission of a patient into the Sea Bathing Infirmary which he has obtained from Mr Harman as his own ticket and that of his son have already been disposed of.

"Mr C. fears that the lateness of the period may render admission from the full state of the Infirmary somewhat uncertain but the patient can have all the benefits of the bathing &c. as an out-patient tho' without having the advantage of being boarded in the House. The last letter received from Mrs Styleman brought good accounts and with thanks for Mrs Icken's friendly remembrances, they shall be duly conveyed on the next occasion of writing Mrs I.

"Mrs I. will please observe that the ticket gives the necessary instructions as to the prescribed mode of admission under it. Also that in the event of becoming an out-patient while awaiting a vacancy there will be no expense of board and lodging incurred."

From this it would seem that Governors had a limited number of presentations each, presumably even limited to a single one in any given year.

The following letter covered the arrival of the above correspondence at the Royal Sea Bathing Hospital 124 years later:

"Berkeley Lodge, Trinity Square, Margate. 6th November 1947."
"Dear Mr Armstrong,

"On looking through some old papers for salvage recently, I came across the enclosed letter written to my late husband's great-great-grandfather and on it the draft of his reply. I thought, in view of its age (124 years) it might be of interest to you and the Committee. Needless to say, I do not want it back. With kind regards, Yours sincerely, Phyllis Cobb.

"P.S. Both my own grandfather and father (Drs W.H. and Bertram Thornton respectively) used to visit the hospital and I have vivid recollections of accompanying the latter on his rounds many a time in the late 1890s, so much so that I can still find my way about the old part of the hospital. P.C."

Reverting, for a moment, to James Taddy who was not only Treasurer but one of the first benefactors of the hospital, it was in 1826 that the oil painting of him, previously mentioned, was presented to the hospital. There is in existence a second identical painting and it is not known for certain which is the original although the one at present hanging in the entrance hall of the hospital is thought to be a copy. The picture which is reproduced is believed to be the original.

John Whyman, of the University of Kent at Canterbury, did a remarkable study of the history of the Royal Sea Bathing Hospital in 1975 in a monograph entitled "An Important Chapter in English Medical and Social History. The Royal Sea Bathing Hospital Margate" (Whyman, 1975). In it he quotes from the Journal of an Excursion to Margate in July and August 1829, an uncatalogued manuscript in the Tyler Collection in the Cathedral

By two Resolutions
of the Margate Sea Bathing Infirmary
bearing date Feb.20ᵗʰ 1822, Aug 13ᵗʰ 1823
Six beds have been reserved in that Infirmary
for the perpetual use of the Radcliffe Infirmary
in consideration of
the sum of £400 raised by subscription
among the Governors of this Institution
and the sum of £200 given by the Rev. Dr. Samuel Wilson Warneford

BENEFACTIONS.

Inscription in the Radcliffe Infirmary, Oxford.

The Marine Parade and new Droit House.

Archives at Canterbury. The family party "took chaise and proceeded to Margate" on 5th August 1829, where they "went over the Infirmary" and "put into the Infirmary box 10 shillings". This must have represented a very considerable donation in those days, particularly when it is realised that, in 1858, a special list was published of all those who subscribed 5/- a year to the charity. Naturally, being a hospital supported by voluntary contributions, every opportunity was taken to solicit financial assistance both from residents in Thanet and from those who visited it in the summer for a holiday.

The Royal Sea Bathing Hospial soon became famous throughout the country and began to draw patients from every county. In 1822/3, the Radcliffe Infirmary at Oxford subscribed the sum of £600 to maintain six beds at the Royal Sea Bathing Infirmary specifically for the use of its patients. There is a painted record high on the corridor wall of the Radcliffe Infirmary just outside the Committee Room which reads as follows:

"By two resolutions of the Margate Sea Bathing Infirmary bearing date Feb 20h 1822 Aug 13h 1823 six beds have been reserved in that Infirmary for the perpetual use of the Radcliffe Infirmary in consideration of the sum of £400 raised by subscription among the Governors of this Institution and the sum of £200 by the Rev. Samuel Wilson Warneford."

In a minute of the Court of Directors (KCC A7 of 27th February 1822, p.308) it was agreed that "Patients of the Radcliffe Infirmary shall be exempt from the examination of the Medical Board in London and shall be admitted upon their producing a Medical Certificate from the Medical Officers of the Ratecliffe *(sic)* Infirmary".

It seems that this arrangement was continued for many years but whether by annual subscription or not is not clear. At least, in 1851 the Court of Directors of the Royal Sea Bathing Infirmary again reported the subscription of £600 from the Radcliffe Infirmary to maintain six beds for its patients.

Margate was a not inconsiderable port in those days and a harbour had been built, or rather, a harbour arm and pier. The picture shows the appearance in 1830. The picture also shows a new form of transport entering the harbour. The "Margate Hoy" was not the only means of reaching Margate by sea from London and had been replaced, at least, in part, in the Thames and its estuary, by the "great Sea Chimera" of the Steam Packet in the 1830s. In the early 1830s there are many references to the *Red Rover*, commanded by Captain Large (Jerrold, l.c. p.111). As will be seen below, the *Red Rover* is actually mentioned as the mode of transport for two of the hospital's girl patients on discharge in a letter from the Hospital Steward, J. Matthews, to the Secretary of the London Committee, Mr Lievesley, on 13th June 1840.

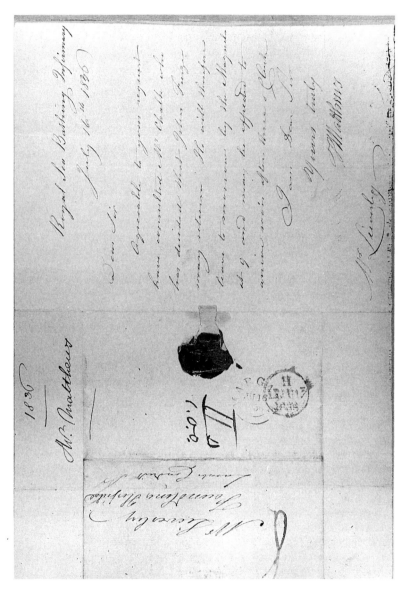

Matthews to Lievesley, 16th July 1836. Note the seal.

58

The steam packet *Victory* about to enter the harbour.

Many of these letters are extant and several of them are quoted here so as to demonstrate the way in which the business of admission and discharge was conducted in the 1830s and 1840s. It will be seen that the copper-plate writing remains beautifully preserved and legible and represents what seems to be almost a lost art today, where the typewriter and the word-processor have superceded calligraphy.

"To Mr Lievesley,   Royal Sea Bathing Infirmary
Foundling Hospital,   16th July 1836
Lambs Conduit Street,
London.
Dear Sir,
    Agreeable to your request have consulted Mr Chalk who has decided that John Furse may return. He will therefore leave tomorrow by the *Magnet* at 9 and may be expected to arrive soon after three o'clock.
    "I am, dear Sir, Yours truly,

                                        J. Matthews" (RSBHA 41)

Matthews to Lievesley, 21st July 1836.
    "The surgeon has requested me to say Weld is quite fit to return if you wish to make an exchange. Armstrong is in want of shoes and the four boys two pairs of socks each as the others being too small are worn out. Armstrong's size is seven." (RSBHA 42)

Matthews to Lievesley, 27th July 1836.
    "I propose sending William Weld tomorrow (Thursday) by the *Royal Adelaide* which may be expected at London Bridge between 4 and 5 o'clock.

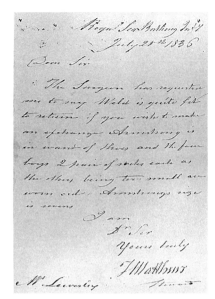

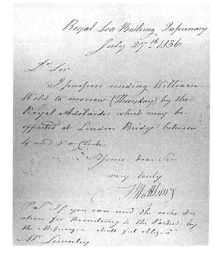

Matthews to Lievesley, 27th July 1836.

Matthews to Lievesley, 21st July 1836.

Margate from the end of the harbour, 1840.

"P.S. If you can send the socks and shoes for Armstrong to the packet by the messenger shall feel obliged." (RSBHA 43)

Matthews to Lievesley, 27th June 1837.

"I have laid your letter before the surgeon who has requested me to inform you that he does not consider that either of the Foundling Children should be sent home at present." (RSBHA 44)

Mr Chalk to Mr Lievesley, 31st August 1837.

"Sir,

"I am sorry to report to you the death of Jas. Woodman aged thirteen. Admitted May 13th. He was taken suddenly ill with symptoms of inflammation of the Brain on Monday last which proved fatal to him on Wednesday morning about 10 o'clock. The symptoms were of that severe character as to defy every means adopted for their alleviation.

"I am Sir, Yours very obediently,

Oliver Chalk" (RSBHA 50)

Matthews to Lievesley, 4th September 1837.

"I beg to acquaint you of William Legge's safe arrival and enclose the certificate of Woodman's burial.

"In my last I requested you to let Leaves have a couple of shirts and two pairs of stockings. The shirts he has are so worn out they will scarce hang on his back. Stockings he has none. Hallet has no cap but I intend purchasing him a common hat on account of his eye which I am happy to say is much better. The girls are much improved." (RSBHA 45)

Matthews to Lievesley, 20th October 1837.

"The patients are to return on Wednesday next in care of the Nurses and I shall feel obliged by your sending to meet them on board the *Magnet* off London Bridge between 3 and 4 o'clock to pay their passages." (RSBHA 370)

An illustration of what Margate must have looked like in 1840 is extremely interesting as it not only shows the harbour but also the appearance of the town itself. Holy Trinity Church is very well seen. The shipping in the harbour is shown to be listing markedly and this is entirely in keeping with the situation today as the harbour is very shallow and, at low tide, the sands are exposed and the ships lie high and dry until the next tide.

Two further letters from Matthews to Lievesley are of interest.

Matthews to Lievesley, 13th June 1840.

"I have submitted your letter to Mr Chalk's perusal who considers Elizth Wyatt and Sara Offley quite well — have therefore decided on their return by the *Red Rover* or *City of Canterbury* on *Monday* which may be expected at London Bridge between 3 & 4 o'clock — as they are both young and shall give them in charge of the stewardess of the vessel and expect to see Armstrong Monday or Tuesday." (RSBHA 368)

It seems that the small steam packets serving the North Kent coast were already carrying stewardesses in 1840!

Matthews to Lievesley, 23rd October 1841.

"On Tuesday the Patients from the Foundling Hospital will return by the *Royal George* and may be expected at London Bridge between 3 & 4 o'clock where they will expect someone to meet them and pay their passage. Mrs Arnold begs me to add she has not been able to procure any employ for Fanny Hope at Margate." (RSBHA 367)

These letters give some indication of the care taken over even the smallest details of an individual's case. They are a commentary on the state of the resettlement attempts also and show that treatment was not limited to the medical side but the social one was considered of importance too.

They are also a telling commentary on the state of the post in those days. While the prepaid penny post of Rowland Hill was still three or four years off into the future (with the exception of the last two letters — the "Penny Black" was first issued for public use on 6th May 1840) Mr Matthews could write from Margate, confident that his letter would get to its destination in London the following day in time for action to be taken to meet the returning patients at London Bridge by three o'clock in the afternoon that day. One hundred and fifty years later when the "First Class" post was 20p, it could certainly not be relied upon to do the same!

In 1837, the Royal Sea Bathing Hospital was again enlarged (Abraham, l.c.) so great was the demand upon its services, but it was still not possible to keep it open throughout the winter months and its period of service continued to be from the beginning of May to the end of October each year.

On 7th June 1841 a National Census was taken so that a very clear picture of the state of the hospital can be obtained.

On that day there were 214 patients, 128 males and 86 females and 154 of them were between the ages of five and fifteen. (The age for admission must have been lowered in the interim.) There were only two patients over the age of forty, so that the incidence of surgical tuberculosis remained constant in pattern from the earliest days of the hospital until the post Second World War arrival of the antibiotics and the other factors that practically eliminated it from Britain. Today, not only is the incidence vastly reduced but much of it is in older people who have had their primary lesions years ago before BCG inoculation and the other environmental conditions which have played so great a part in reducing the impact of the disease.

The staff to look after these patients numbered twenty-five: ten nurses, seven housemaids and one each of Steward, Matron, Surgeon, Assistant Surgeon, Bath Nurse, Male Servant, Female Servant and Cook. The cook must have had a full-time job to provide meals for 239 people! Perhaps there was some non-resident help!

Of the twenty-five staff, only three were under the age of twenty, a further seven under thirty, and one over sixty. There were four "independent women" in the surgeon's house. It seems possible that William and Emily Chalk may have been taking holidaymakers. Perhaps it is not maligning them too far to suggest that these may have been paying guests, thus helping to swell the family finances a little. Alternatively, of course, they may have been relatives visiting them.

The occupations of the male patients were recorded, some forty-two in all. But as there were only thirty-four male patients in the hospital over the age of fifteen, nine of these occupations must have related to boys of fifteen or under:

Agricultural labourer	3	Ostler	1
Artist	1	Painter	1
Banker's clerk	1	Plumber	1
Bricklayer	1	Ploughman	1
Bricklayer's labourer	1	Porter	2
Cabinet maker	1	Printer	3
Carpenter	1	Schoolmaster	1
Compositor	1	Shoemaker	3
Counting office clerk	1	Tailor	3
Druggist	1	Tea dealer	1
Footman	2	Waiter	1
Gardener	1	Watch gilder	1
Lighterman	2	Wheelwright	1
Male servant	1	Whipmaker	1
Medical student	1	Wine porter	1
Nurseryman	1		

(Whyman, quoting PRO/HO/107/468/6)

It is interesting to note that one of the patients was a medical student and to see some of the occupations which have ceased to exist. Presumably there are now no more ostlers nor, probably, whipmakers or watch gilders.

In the 1840s a major discovery affected every branch of medicine. Morton, Simpson, Young, Hickman, Long and Snow all played a part in the discovery and introduction of anaesthetics. Nitrous oxide was discovered first, in 1840, ether in 1846 and chloroform in 1847. The dreadful agonies of patients undergoing surgical operations without anaesthetics were over and the patients who needed surgery were no longer to die in fifty per cent of cases from shock and haemorrhage.

In 1848 John Lefevre was a patient. He had been condemned to lose his leg on account of disease and was admitted to the Royal Sea Bathing Hospital. He visited the hospital on 16th May 1901, living, at the time, at Whittlesey, Cambridgeshire. By then, as will be seen below, a Hospital Visitors' Book had been in use for many years. He availed himself of the opportunity to make the following comment:

"Intensely interested. Very much pleased with all I have seen. Was a patient here for six months about 1848 — left leg condemned by family doctor, also by Guy's and St Thomas' Hospitals, but saved here, never having felt anything of it since, I remember this institution with very deep gratitude."

Many hospitals can record successes and have many grateful patients, but it is relatively uncommon to obtain a satisfactory "follow-up" fifty-three years later.

Beale's Bathing Machines.
One of the helpers might be Mary Brockman.

Some of the Archives of the hospital damaged by water.

James Taddy, the first London Treasurer.

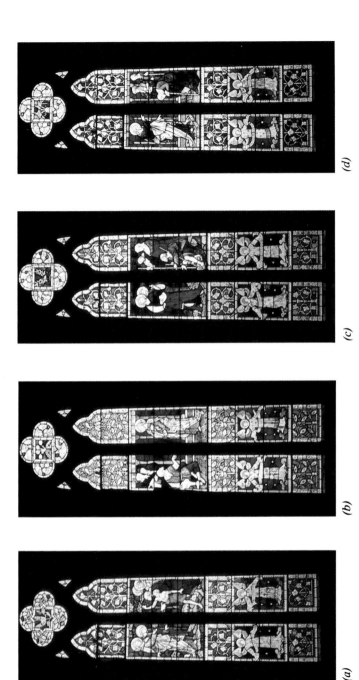

(a) Jesus casts out a devil from a boy thought to have been suffering from epilepsy. "He rebuked the devil and he departed out of him." Luke. 9. 37-42., (b) Jesus cures the man with the withered hand. "His hand was restored whole as the other." Luke. 6. 6-10., (c) Jesus cures the blind beggar, Bartimeus. "Go thy way, they faith hath made thee whole." Mark. 10. 46-52., (d) Jesus cures the woman with the bowed back. "He laid His hands on her and immediately she was made straight." Luke. 13. 11-13.

(a)

(b)

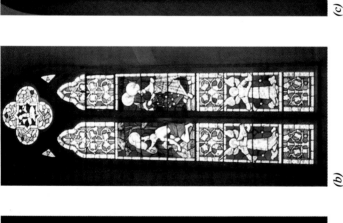

(c)   (d)

(a) Jesus cures the deaf man by putting His fingers into his ears. "He maketh both the deaf to hear and the dumb to speak."
Luke. 7. 22., (b) Jesus cures the blind man at the Pool of Siloam. Jesus puts His fingers on his eyes and says: "Go, wash
in the Pool of Siloam". John. 9.7., (c) Jesus cures Peter's Wife's Mother. "He touched her hand and the fever left her".
Matthew. 8. 14,15., (d) Jesus cures the Maniac of Gadara. "What have we to do with Thee, Thou Son of God most High?".
Luke. 8. 26-33.

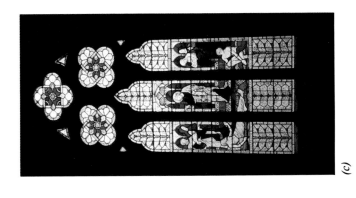

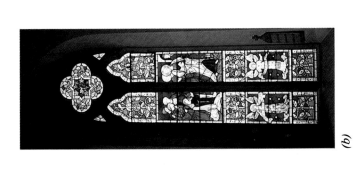

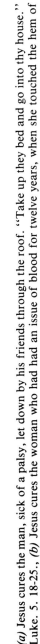

(a)

(b)

(c)

(a) Jesus cures the man, sick of a palsy, let down by his friends through the roof. "Take up they bed and go into thy house." Luke. 5. 18-25., *(b)* Jesus cures the woman who had had an issue of blood for twelve years, when she touched the hem of His garment. "Daughter, be of good cheer, thy faith hath made thee whole." Luke. 9. 43-48., *(c)* The Pool at Bethesda. The man too crippled to get into the pool first is cured by Jesus. "Rise, take up they bed and walk'. John. 5. 4-9. One of the cripples has his leg in the water already, determined to be first!

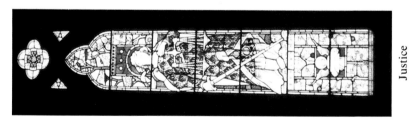

Mercy   Fortitude   Temperance   Justice   Prudence

The Chancel Windows.

The huge West window. "Now when the sun was setting, all they that had any sick with divers diseases brought them unto Him; and He laid His hands on every one of them, and healed them". Luke. 4. 40.

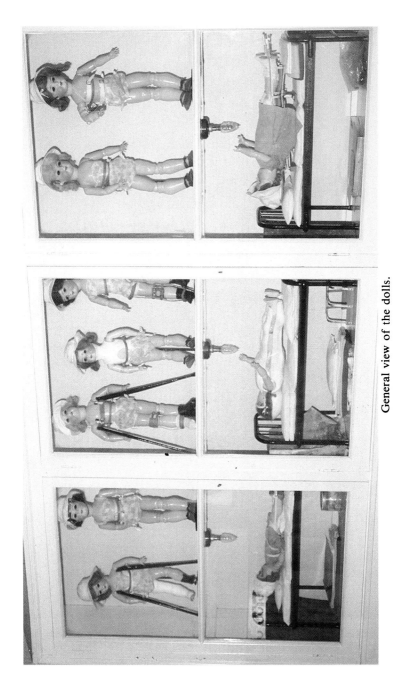

General view of the dolls.

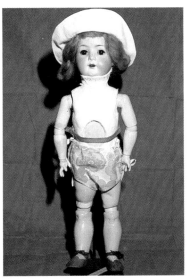

Doll with "Minerva" plaster for the treatment of tuberculosis of the cervical spine.

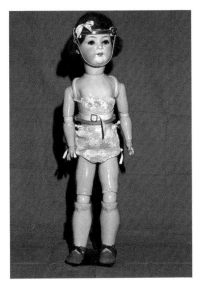

Doll with cervical brace and jury mast, for continuation treatment of the same.

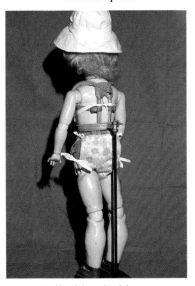

Doll with spinal brace.

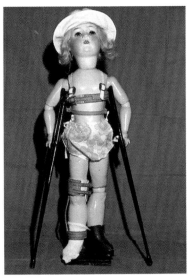

Doll with Thomas' hip splint and raised boot.

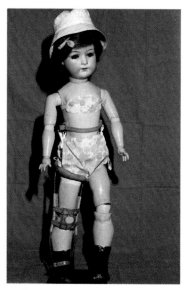

Doll with Thomas' walking caliper.

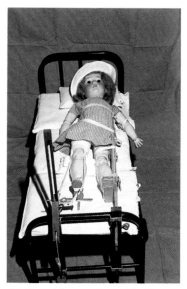

Doll on hip traction with "long Liston" splint counter-traction.

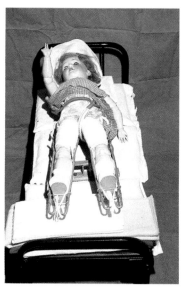

Doll on Bradford frame for hip abduction and traction, with groin strap.

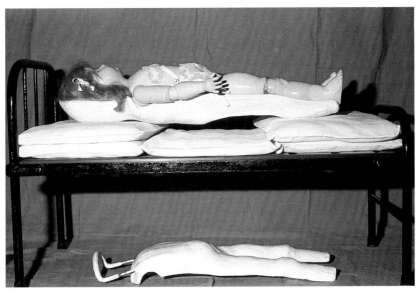

Doll on plaster bed. The turning plaster is under the bed.

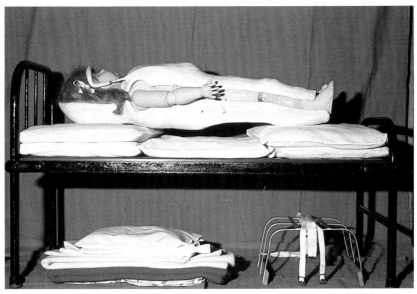

Doll on plaster bed with turning plaster, with its detachable
forehead rest, in position ready for turning. For actual
turning, the two plasters would be strapped together.

Patients on Alexandra Ward balcony taking the sun and sea breezes.
They will be looking at the view seen in the photo below.

Patients' view from the Hospital across Westbrook Bay

The old Operating Theatre with its superb window.

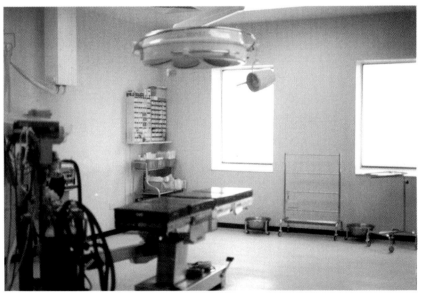

The new Operating Theatre with its two smaller windows.

Margate Air. One of the Orthopaedic Teams on a "Ward Round"!

The old Splint-making Shop.

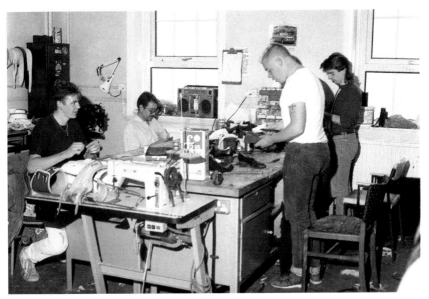

The new Splint-making Shop.

The Friends of the Royal Sea Bathing Hospital's Fete Day. July, 1989.

Margate Beach. High Summer. Midday.

Margate Beach. High Summer. Sunset.

Chapter 4
ERASMUS WILSON

There were several epidemics of cholera in 1849 which affected the Royal Sea Bathing Hospital very seriously. There were no fewer than seventy cases, including the Assistant Surgeon, the Matron, the Steward, Nurses and Patients. The Resident Surgeon himself is said to have been affected but he still seems to have carried out the work of the hospital virtually single-handed, including the added work of the epidemic. Most members of the staff survived but two nurses and three patients died. Many people fled the hospital, both staff and patients. The Resident Surgeon reported that he himself ". . . was twice attacked but not disabled (!) . . . so little assistance could I obtain that I was myself obliged to carry the dead bodies from the wards to a neighbouring building where they were deposited till they could be buried. The few nurses who remained were too much alarmed to approach them."

These details are recorded in a printed memorandum in the shape of a letter to the Hospital Governors asking the reason why its author had apparently been dismissed without notice after five years of loyal service (A.G. Field, May 1852, KCC A1). The result of the complaint is not known.

As mentioned in the last chapter, it was in 1851 that the Court of Directors (Minutes, 1851) recorded that the Radcliffe Infirmary at Oxford was contributing £600 towards the cost of maintaining six beds for its patients at the Royal Sea Bathing Hospital. This seems to suggest that the medical staff of the Radcliffe felt that the Royal Sea Bathing Hospital continued to have a contribution to make to the treatment of their patients.

It was also in 1851 that Her Majesty Queen Victoria donated the sum of £50 to the Royal Sea Bathing Hospital (KCC MH/T1 A1). It may have been on this occasion that she granted her patronage to the hospital. It is known that this happened before 1853 but the exact date is not recorded.

By this year the hospital had treated 22,934 patients, the greatest number in any one year having been 716. It was clearly continuing to be much in demand and therefore the Governors extended the hospital considerably. They built additional wings on both sides. On the sea side, it was for female patients, apparently long overdue, an additional dining-room, a brew-house and numerous offices on the basement storey *(sic)*. A new wing on the road side of the hospital extended its bed strength to 230 (KCC MH/T1 R1).

"In order to ensure to the patient the full benefit arising from the use of sea bathing, applied in the most efficient manner, two large reservoirs were constructed into one of which the sea constantly flows . . . the water is supplied in a very pure condition" (ibid. xi).

In 1852 it was given out that ". . . every individual, every public body is called upon to aid this charity. It is a proper supplement to the Hospitals, a necessary link in the chain of eleemosynary establishments for the benefit of the indigent poor of the Metropolis" (ibid, p.vii).

This appeal was supported by thirteen physicians, headed by Henry Halford, President of the Royal College of Physicians and thirteen surgeons, headed by G.V. Guthrie, President of the Royal College of Surgeons and Anthony White and John G. Andrews, Vice-Presidents.

The Governors also laid it down that, ". . . amongst the Medical Board in London, apart from Fellows and Licentiates of the Royal College of Physicians, there should be twelve surgeons — Fellows of the Royal College of Surgeons, not practising pharmacy" (!) (ibid. xix).

As a result of the extensive additions to the hospital, it was found that the improvements now made it possible for the Governors to resolve, on 12th September 1853, that the hospital be kept open for patients during the whole year and this was recommended to the Court of Directors (ibid, A5).

Sea bathing had been supplemented for some time by the provision of baths in the hospital, although it had not been replaced by them as yet, and sea bathing continued to be supervised by a "bath nurse". It seems that the earliest baths had the sea water pumped up the thirty feet or so from the sea by a horse! However, progress continued and by 1853, it is recorded that all sorts of baths had been fitted up in the hospital and that apparatus had been installed to force the water up from the sea. (I suppose you could "install" a horse but you could hardly call a horse "apparatus"!)

That year, Dr Canham and Mr Hunter were Medical Officers. The wages for nurses and servants cost £34.7s.0d per month. As there were, at least at the time of the census, ten nurses and seven servants, this represents wages of ten shillings per week, nearly reaching the steward's wages in 1800.

The Rev. John Hodgson was the secretary of the local Committee and his portrait, which was painted in 1856, hangs in the entrance hall of the hospital and the ward block named after him now houses the Out-Patient Services for Chest Diseases and Genito-urinary Surgery and Medicine.

Erasmus Wilson, who was later to become such a generous benefactor to the hospital, has been mentioned above and another link with Lettsom was made when he, in 1857, saved a woman, Olivier Green, from drowning in Regent's Canal (Hadley, 1958). For this he was awarded the Silver Medal of the Royal Humane Society, of which Lettsom had been a co-founder.

A boys' ward bearing the name of Lettsom is said to have been opened in 1857 but carries the date "1858" in bold lettering and, in the early 1950s, was developed as the first men's ward for the treatment of non-tuberculous orthopaedic conditions. Later still it was converted to the Department of Physical Medicine.

Keeping the hospital open the whole year round was partly possible because "sea bathing" could now be provided on the premises in covered baths. Still, gates were built to allow patients access to the beach. Exactly how this differed from the access that must have been available to allow the original sea bathing is not clear, perhaps an improved route or boundary fence may have been newly installed, necessitating gates. It is not known when the perimeter was finally supplied with its present brick walls.

Keeping the hospital open all the winter inevitably involved a very costly addition to the demands on the hospital exchequer and had been met, in part, by the formation and publication (in 1859) of a "five shilling list" (RSBHA 9). On 9th July of that year, the Dover Express and Intelligencer records that the 5/- list now contained "about 4,500 names, many of them of the nobility, many bishops, some judges, many officers of the army and navy, many clergy, many tradesmen and not a few servants in families and others of low degree (!) whose relations and friends had benefited from the charity, had enrolled themselves as subscribers." (Whyman, l.c.) This same journal mentions that the hospital now had 250 beds, three honorary local surgeons, a resident surgeon assisted by a dispenser and several bathing machines.

It is of interest that, in 1862, the hospital had its own splintmaker in the person of a Mr Schmidt. Presumably he was accommodated in a room converted into some semblance of a workshop but it will be seen that not until sixteen, and again fifty-nine years later, that recommendations for a splint-making shop were made and not until 1924, no less than sixty years later, was one eventually provided.

In 1866 the hospital had a rather famous patient, no less than Karl Marx, the philosopher and one of the originators of communism. He spent four weeks in the hospital convalescing from an attack of boils (McLellan, 1973 and RSBHA 449). It appears that the original purpose of treating "scrofula" had, by now, become observed with a certain amount of elasticity. Marx, at this time, was a resident in London and again we may see the nation-wide service that the hospital provided. It was said that there were patients in the hospital from sixteen counties and that they occupied one third of the hospital's 250 beds.

In 1867 three events occurred, each of a very different type, but each of which was to be of major importance to the hospital. The first was the institution of the hospital "Visitors' Book" (RSBHA 14). This served to carry the signatures and comments of visitors right down to 1935. It is a treasure house of fascinating remarks on the state of the hospital, together with the autographs of many famous people, including those of royalty, archbishops, generals, and well-known physicians and surgeons. Many of the historical vignettes here recorded will be seen in these pages and the book remains a valuable commentary on the activities of the hospital as seen through outside eyes over a period of almost seventy years.

Erasmus Wilson's signature in the Visitors' Book, September 27th 1867, with his comment.

The second event of importance was the first visit of Erasmus Wilson (1809-1884) to the Royal Sea Bathing Hospital. The results of this visit remain very much with us today. He signed the Visitors' Book on 27th September 1867 and entered the following comments:

"The state of the patients very satisfactory. If some charitably disposed person would heat the wards with steam, a great benefit, in my opinion, would be conferred on the patients. I find several patients complaining of cold and some, perhaps unavoidably, in a direct draft" (RSBHA 14). A great deal will be heard of Erasmus Wilson later.

The third, and most resounding event of all, was the publication in 1867 of Lister's paper on antiseptics, namely, in this case, carbolic acid, in the treatment of compound fractures. This was a development which was to have a major bearing on all aspects of medicine and surgery now and into the future.

Erasmus Wilson as a young man   Erasmus Wilson in later life

From time to time, certain entries from the comments in the Visitors' Book will be inserted into the narrative as they throw light on the day to day progress of the hospital. In 1868, for example, the City of London Committee (? Guardians) commented: "We are well satisfied with all the arrangements and the care bestowed upon the patients in this establishment" (RSBHA 14, 25th July). The Manager of the Finsbury school, after visiting the hospital, said: "Inspected the establishment and found everything clean and orderly and satisfactory" (ibid, 11th October). Mr and Mrs Halsult, of Woolwich, wrote: "Very much pleased with the order and cleanliness of the establishment (ibid, 9th June 1869). Mrs Thomas Jenkins said she was delighted to see everything so neat and clean (ibid, 8th July).

Miss Robins "and others" visited the Royal Sea Bathing Hospital in 1870 (RSBHA 14) and stated that they were very pleased to see the patients appearing so happy.

From comments such as these, it is apparent that the hospital was being run on both efficient and humanitarian lines, as indeed it should if it was to follow the precept and practice of its founder. It obviously impressed many visitors, one of whom was Sir J.H. Crewe, of Calke Abbey, Derby, who wrote: 'Expressed intention to become a Life Governor and Annual Subscriber of One Guinea" (ibid, 23rd February 1871).

It is difficult today to appreciate what the subscription of a guinea really meant. One pound and one shilling in 1871 might be considered to be on a par with considerably more than one hundred pounds now. In fact, if a nurse's salary was £25 per annum then, three hundred pounds would perhaps be a more realistic approximation. However, this must be balanced against the calculation of 1800 (page 15) that the pound then was worth fifty of today's pounds. It is rather more a commentary on the abysmal way in which nurses were paid which is only beginning to be remedied today. So a guinea was more probably equivalent to £50 or £60 today.

Dr Knight Treves became the Visiting Surgeon in 1870 and served for twenty years. He lived in Margate and was the Borough Surgeon. His younger brother also studied medicine and in 1876, Knight Treves got him to work at the Royal Sea Bathing Hospital as his assistant for five months (Gibbs, 1989). This was Frederick Treves who later achieved fame as Sir Frederick Treves, operating on King Edward VII for appendicitis and so popularising the operation. Sir Frederick became Senior Surgeon to the London Hospital, wrote "The Other Side of the Lantern" and also, more widely known still, "The Elephant Man".

Sir Frederick Treves was later to become a member of the London Medical Board of the Royal Sea Bathing Hospital and paid it a number of visits. It is stimulating to think that the Royal Sea Bathing Hospital played its part in the early training of a man who was to become the country's most famous surgeon in the first decade of the twentieth century.

Dr William Knight Treves' son, Frederick Boileau Treves, followed him in the profession and also followed his father in being appointed one of the Visiting Surgeons of the hospital. He served in the 1914-18 war and ultimately became Consulting Surgeon to the Royal Sea Bathing Hospital in 1930.

It was in 1871 that the clinical thermometer was first introduced and, ever since, it has been looked upon as the touchstone of the body's health and ability to react to inflammatory conditions. The following year Dr W.E. Dixon was appointed to be Resident Surgeon and it was in this year that the story again takes an unexpected turn. There is, as is well known, no new thing under the sun (Ecclesiastes 1.9) and those of us who live in the 1980s and 1990s probably imagine that double glazing is a phenomenon of the second half of the twentieth century. Far from it. In 1872, during the autumn, double windows were put up at the Royal Sea Bathing Hospital on the "sea side" in order to ameliorate the conditions in the wards during the winter (KRO, 1872). I do not know whether steam heating had been installed by now, in accordance with Erasmus Wilson's suggestion of fifteen years earlier, but both steam heating and double glazing seem to trespass upon Lettsom's idea of the open air treatment of scrofula.

The quadrangle, as it is today, had not yet appeared, and the part of the old building which now faces onto it was the front of the hospital, facing west. In front of the hospital, then, in this eminently suitable situation, there was erected in 1872 a fountain of red granite in memory of Rev. John Hodgson. It bears the inscription: "In memory of Revd John Hodgson, M.A., for many years the revered Honorary Secretary and untiring Friend of this Institution". The fountain has not played for some years but the memory of Hodgson persists and continues to help in shaping the quite unique loyalty of all grades of staff to the Royal Sea Bathing Hospital. Such an atmosphere cannot but encourage all patients entering the hospital today.

Dr W.H. Thornton was one of the Visiting Surgeons of the charity in 1872. It will be recalled that he was the grandfather of Mrs Cobb who kindly forwarded the correspondence between Mrs Icken and Dr Cobb of the 1820s and who used to take her on his rounds of the hospital.

W.E. Henley (1849-1903) was a notable poet and editor. He spent a considerable time in hospital at the Old Infirmary, Edinburgh, where he was under Lister for a time. He had an amputation for tuberculous infection of the foot and describes his sensations when going under the anaesthetic which was of course, chloroform in those days.

"OPERATION" by W.E. Henley
". . . Then they bid you close your eyelids
And they mask you with a napkin
And the anaesthetic reaches
Hot and subtle through your being.

"And you gasp and reel and shudder
In a rushing, swaying rapture,
While the voices at your elbow
Fade — receding — fainter — farther."

(Henley, 1926)

Whilst most of Henley's evocative poems about life in hospital as a patient relate to his time in Edinburgh, they cover the period, in 1873, when he was a patient in the Royal Sea Bathing Hospital. It may be reasonable to take it, therefore, that his famous poem: "Invictus", which bespeaks the courage with which he faced his disability, speaks also for every patient at the Royal Sea Bathing Hospital.

"INVICTUS" by W.E. Henley
"Out of the night that covers me,
Black as the pit from pole to pole,
I thank whatever gods may be
For my unconquerable soul.

"In the clutch of circumstance
I have not winced nor cried aloud.
Under the bludgeonings of chance
My head is bloody but unbowed.

A ward showing the teak floorboards and central heating. The picture is early twentieth century.

"Beyond this place of wrath and tears
Looms but the horror of the shade,
And yet the menace of the years
Finds and shall find me unafraid.

"It matters not how strait the gate,
How charged with punishments the scroll,
I am the master of my fate:
I am the captain of my soul."

(Henley, 1949)

The Court of Directors held a meeting on 30th December 1874, when they agreed to a schoolmaster being appointed. They went on to state that ". . . they are of the opinion that the schoolmaster need not be of a high class of knowledge, considering he will have under his care convalescents who ought not to be over-pressed with work . . ." He is to be ". . . rather one who will preserve discipline and give a little moral tone to the establishment." They suggested that one such might be found in the "Army Schoolmaster Serjeants *(sic)* pension list" (KCCMH/T1 A7, p.415).

As a further illustration of the value of money in the 1870s, a hindquarter of beef sold at the rate of 8d a pound. The cost of boarding a patient was still about 6/- a week and 5/- for children. It is amusing to read that, in considering the provision of sea water baths, the hospital secretary asks if, very often, the patients are bathed *merely for the sake of cleanliness* or was it all for medical treatment? (John Thomas Walker, 17th February 1875, RSBH 11A). Obviously he was a very careful secretary because it was also in April of this year that the Medical Officers were asked to reduce their consumption of ale!

The hospital engineer, who was no doubt responsible for arranging the salt water to be fed into the baths, was Mr Stileman. J.C. Brazier had been appointed the previous year as Clerk to the Superintendent who was George Horatio Chestfield. George Chestfield had been in post since 1861 and served for thirty-five years. He died in 1896 at the early age of fifty-five and is commemorated by a brass memorial in the Chapel. Was he, one wonders, another victim of the tubercle bacillus? It is not known if J.C. Brazier was related to the enigmatic Zachariah Brazier who endorsed Mary Brockman's bill for bathing the patients in 1800 at a time when Zachariah Cozens was the hospital secretary.

A curious record relates to the year 1875 when it is stated that the wards were fitted with floorboards. One wonders what the floors were made of before that, whether of flagstones, as seems most probable (surely not the *terra firma* of Margate!) or of brick, sand or sawdust? When the 1882 ward floors were relaid in the 1950s, it was realised that these floorboards were of teak.

Dr Thomas Gimson recorded in the Visitors' Book: "Much pleased. The comforts of the patients appear to be considered to the fullest extent". Similarly, a Mr S. Hill visited the hospital and entered in the book: "Much gratified with the cleanliness and order which pervades the whole of this beneficient institution" (RSBHA 14, 9.10.1875 and 1.10.1876). A patient at the time was Henry Tovey. He visited the hospital in the late summer of 1922, more than forty years later, and signed the Visitors' Book.

The Deaconess Helen Lyall visited the hospital on 16th September 1878 and remarked: "The Infirmary seems most beautifully conducted". There is little doubt that, as mentioned above, the hospital had a very efficient medical, nursing and administrative organisation. This can only have been of the greatest benefit to the patients under treatment, many of whose medical and surgical conditions would have placed a very great load on the nursing care and domestic services available. The point is further confirmed by Erasmus Wilson's remarks when he again visited the hospital in 1880 when he wrote: "Quiet and calm amid tranquility. House and wards clean and sweet. Countenances expressive of comfort and contentment. Nurses attentive and devoted to their work, earning, as they deserve, the blessing of the Almighty. As we ourselves would be helped, let us help one another" (ibid. 31.10.1880).

Erasmus Wilson's reference to the wards being "sweet" raises a picture of what hospital wards in the big cities may well have been really like in the

1880s. Particularly when there was joint tuberculosis, with multiple sinuses pouring out copious discharges daily, as well as other diseases where chronic ulceration and sinuses were a prominent feature, there must have been a very distinct loss of "sweetness" in the atmosphere of the wards. While wounds with these characteristics must have been very common in the Royal Sea Bathing Hospital, the high standard of nursing, together with the open-air structure of the hospital and the constant part sea bathing took in the pattern of treatment, were clearly so effective that Erasmus Wilson could actively comment on the "sweetness" of the wards in contrast to what he was accustomed to in London.

About this time, Queen Victoria became an annual subscriber in the rather remarkable figure of £71!

The Board bought ten tons of Deal beach! It is not known exactly what the purpose of this acquisition was; one might assume that it was for improving pathways although there is no trace of the pebbles visible today.

Another visitor to the hospital in 1880 was Sir Harry Wilbraham who was Chairman of King's College Hospital. Today, we have very close links with King's through the Senior Registrar Rotation programme which brings a King's College Hospital Senior Orthopaedic Registrar to East Kent for a year in the course of his training and this includes his working in the Royal Sea Bathing Hospital.

The following year, William Garrow Lettsom, grandson of the Founder, visited the hospital, demonstrating, as will be seen in later pages, the continuing family interest in the Foundation by the descendants of Lettsom.

This year, 1881, also saw Erasmus Wilson President of the Royal College of Surgeons of England (Cope, 1959). Mention has been made of his birth and first visit to the hospital but some more details of this figure who was such a factor in the development of the Royal Sea Bathing Hospital in the nineteenth century are essential.

On 8th June 1837 William James Erasmus Wilson presented himself before a special meeting of the Council of the Royal College of Surgeons and was examined in Anatomy and Physiology by the curious method of choosing at random from a hat a number of questions set by members of the Council and previously placed in the hat! He was deemed to have satisfied the examiners so that, on 6th July of the same year, he was again examined by the Council by the same method, this time in Pathology and Surgery. The result was again satisfactory and Erasmus Wilson became, therefore, the first person to obtain the Fellowship of the Royal College of Surgeons by examination, at which he was the only candidate! (ibid.)

One wonders if there has ever been an occasion since when the pass-rate in the Fellowship was 100 per cent!

Sir Erasmus Wilson lived in Rowena Court, Westgate (now demolished) and his main interest was Dermatology. No doubt the proximity of his house to the hospital and, possibly, the presence of cases of lupus in the wards brought him an abiding and extremely generous interest in the Royal Sea Bathing Hospital.

Erasmus Wilson was the son of a Highland father and a Norwegian mother and was born in the High Street, Marylebone, on 25th November 1809. His father, William Wilson, RN, and his maternal grandfather, Erasmus Brousdorph, were both surgeons. He studied in Paris and London and passed the Apothecaries' examination in 1830 and the Membership of the Royal College of Surgeons in 1831. He was Assistant Professor of Anatomy at the Royal College of Surgeons and Assistant Editor of "The Lancet". T. Glyn Thomas, in a study of Erasmus Wilson's character (1973), describes him as industrious, ambitious, flamboyant, a dominant personality, physically courageous, likeable and generous and having a Dickensian sense of humour!

Erasmus Wilson became Professor of Anatomy at the Middlesex Hospital in 1840 and Consulting Surgeon to the St Marylebone, or possibly the St Pancras, Infirmary (Hadley 1960). In 1881 he was knighted, the year of his Presidency of the Royal College of Surgeons of England, and made an Honorary LL.D. of the University of Aberdeen and a Fellow of the Royal Society. He was also Vice-President of the Society of Biblical Archaeology with a special interest in Egypt. It was presumably this that prompted him to pay for the transport of Cleopatra's Needle to Britain from Egypt. The Needle had been presented to Britain by the Egyptian Government in 1820 but it was left unclaimed until 1877.

A metal flotation chamber was built around it and it was towed through the Mediterranean and through the Straits of Gibraltar. However, in a severe storm in the Bay of Biscay, the tow-rope parted and the Needle went adrift. Luckily it was recaptured and successfully brought to England, but six crewmen of the s.s. *Olga*, the original towing vessel, were lost in attempting to re-establish the tow.

Cleopatra's Needle was erected on the Embankment in London on 12th September 1878. Its journey to Britain had cost Erasmus Wilson the sum of £10,000 and John Dixon, the Engineer, £5,000.

Under the Needle were placed:

A complete set of coins and weights.	A box of hairpins (!).
The day's newspapers.	A map of London.
One of the hydraulic lifting jacks.	A Mappin's shilling razor.
Bibles in four languages.	Numerous toys.

An Alexandrian Feeding Bottle and Bradshaw's Railway Guide of the World. Pictures of a dozen pretty English women were added by Captain Henry Carter! (Connor, 1978; Howard, 1978; Hadley, l.c.)

Erasmus Wilson founded the Chair of Anatomy at the Royal College of Surgeons and a Chair of Pathology in Aberdeen. He was a donor to Epsom College and the Royal College of Music and a Director of the Royal Sea Bathing Hospital.

Cleopatra's Needle

The chapel

Alexandra and Louise Wards

So it was that, in 1882, Erasmus Wilson came to present the Royal Sea Bathing Hospital with his most generous gift to date. He provided the sum of £30,000 for the enlargement of the hospital. The architect of the new buildings was James Knowles, who was also the editor of "The Nineteenth Century".

In 1882 the new wing was opened. It included the whole of the main ward block of the present hospital, that is to say, the wards Alexandra, Louise, Victoria and Maud, named after the Princess of Wales, later Queen Alexandra, and her three daughters. The smaller portion of Maud and a room adjoining were the sea bathing bath. The famous horse had, of course, long since disappeared and modern plumbing apparatus replaced the previous pumps to fill the considerable pool that resulted.

The wards of the new extension were lofty and had curved, vaulted ceilings, they and the walls being tiled throughout with white, glazed tiles. The object was that they could be completely hosed down for cleanliness, though they looked to us in the 1940s a little like public lavatories.

Not the least of the hospital extensions under the gift of Erasmus Wilson was the hospital chapel. This chapel is a superb example of the Victorian Gothic and must be one of the finest hospital chapels in existence. It is probably unique in one respect and that is that the front half of the nave is left bare of pews so that patients can be wheeled into the chapel in their beds to attend Divine Service.

Mr T. Glyn Thomas, FRCS, has written an appreciation of the chapel and it is reproduced here, with some additions, as an appendix to this chapter.

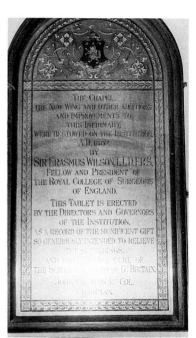

The chancel

Tablet in the chapel to Erasmus Wilson

The nave

Appendix
THE CHAPEL
OF THE ROYAL SEA BATHING HOSPITAL

The chapel of the Royal Sea Bathing Hospital was built out of Erasmus Wilson's munificent gift in 1882. It is a splendid example of the Victorian Pseudo-Gothic style of architecture.

On entering up the ramp from the balcony of Maud Ward, a brass tablet will be observed on the opposite wall. It is in honour of the Founder, John Coakley Lettsom, and was placed there on the recommendation of Sir Edgar Waterlow in his toast to the Founder at the dinner in 1946. There are also brass plates commemorating Erasmus Wilson's generous gift and one over the "Father Willis" organ which was given in memory of Dame Charlotte Wilson, Erasmus' widow. The brass lectern is as fine as will be found in almost any parish church.

The most striking feature of the chapel, apart from its extremely high-pitched roof, is the superb stained glass of the windows. This beautiful stained glass depicts the Miracles of Healing of Christ, taken mainly from the Gospel of St Luke.

Windows
The main series is of windows in ten pairs on the two sides of the nave. They are seen in the colour plates as follows:
1. Jesus casts out a devil from a boy, thought to have been suffering from epilepsy.
2. Jesus cures the man with the withered hand.
3. Jesus cures blind Bartimeus.
4. Jesus cures the woman with the deformity of her spine.
5. Jesus cures the deaf man by putting His fingers into his ears.
6. Jesus cures the blind man by putting His fingers on his eyes and telling him to go and wash in the Pool of Siloam.
7. Jesus cures Peter's wife's mother.
8. Jesus casts out devils from the maniac of Gadara.
9. Jesus cures the man, sick of a palsy, whose friends let him down from the housetop.
10. Jesus cures the woman who had an issue of blood for twelve years when she touched the hem of His garment.

To the south side of the chancel there is a triptych showing the Pool of Bethesda where the lame, the blind and the halt bathed after the waters had been stirred up by an angel. Jesus cures a man too crippled to be the first to get into the pool after this happened. One man, sitting by the pool, has one foot in it already; he obviously means to be the first next time!

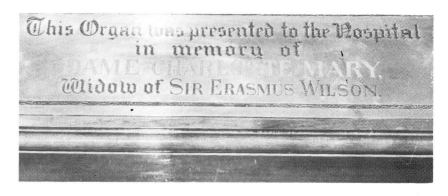

This Organ was presented to the Hospital in memory of DAME CHARLOTTE MARY, Widow of Sir Erasmus Wilson.

Tablet to Dame Charlotte Wilson

The windows above the chancel show the five virtues: prudence, justice, temperance, fortitude and mercy.

On the west wall is a huge, five-part window showing many being brought to Him and being healed. High above this is a very small window whose details cannot be seen but it depicts Saint Stephen.

Above the side windows are small, round windows which illustrate the flowers and plants from which drugs and medicines were obtained in the olden days: Poppies (opium), Rye (ergot), Wild Garlic (laxative), Figs (aperients), Deadly Nightshade (atropine), and Foxglove (digitalis).

There are also several murals. Below the window of St Stephen, but high above the huge west window and needing the eyes to be shaded against the brilliance of the evening light flooding through it, is the Tree of Knowledge from Adam and Eve's Garden of Eden.

Above the side windows and the round herbal windows are murals of the Apostles.

The largest mural of all is on the west wall below the main window. It is drawn from the Second Book of Kings, chapter 5, verses 1-15:

Naaman, the General of the King of Syria's Army, was a leper, and his wife had a captive slave girl out of the land of Israel and she told her mistress to send the General to the Prophet Elisha as he could cure him. So, having got permission of absence, Naaman departed with many slaves, troops and much baggage and went to Israel and to the door where the Prophet lived. The Prophet did not come out to him but sent his servant with a message, saying: "Go and wash seven times in Jordan and thy flesh shall come unto thee, and thou shalt be clean."

This treatment annoyed Naaman who naturally expected to receive preferential treatment and active action. Indeed, he expected to be treated

Marble relief to commemorate Basil Armstrong in the chancel of the chapel.

BASIL WILLIAM ARMSTRONG

O·B·E., M·C., M·B., B·S., M·R·C·S., L·R·C·P
BORN 12TH JULY 1889
DIED 14TH MAY 1958
*Medical Superintendent of the
Royal Sea Bathing Hospital*
1923 · 1954

as a private patient. And so he started to pack up and go home, saying: "Are not Abana and Pharpar, rivers of Damascus, better than all the waters of Israel?" But his luggage porters, tired, no doubt, begged him to "have a go" at the Jordan treatment and so he did and "his flesh came again like unto the flesh of a little child and he was clean."

And so the Bible is the first to record that an out-patient did not see the Consultant but received treatment from his House Physician. But the HP was acting under the instructions of his chief and so the result was the same!

Sadly, however, Gehazi, Elisha's servant, dishonestly acquired the fee which Elisha had refused and the leprosy came upon him instead.

It will have been noticed that the Royal Sea Bathing Hospital's fundamental principle of bathing is underlined by the bathing in Jordan, in the Pool of Siloam and the Pool at Bethesda.

Some of the conditions illustrated are still commonly found in Orthopaedic practice today, as, for example, the man with the withered hand and the man "sick of palsy", that is to say, paralysed in some degree. The case of the woman with the severely bowed back who "was bowed together, and could in no wise lift herself up" is again an example of the cure of an Orthopaedic complaint. In the illustration in the chapel's stained glass, she would seem a classical case of ankylosing spondylitis.

Alas, the Orthopaedic Surgeon of today cannot hope to emulate the miracles of Christ of two thousand years ago.

There is a number of brass tablets in memory of members of the staff of various categories who are referred to elsewhere in the text and a fine semi-relief head and memorial tablet of Basil Armstrong in white marble. A beautiful winged St George slaying the dragon bears the simple inscription: "Henry Farnaby Lennard, Bt. Amicus Certus". He had been Chairman of the Court of Directors in the early years of this century.

Services used to be held every Sunday but now, alas, few services are held in this beautiful chapel. It was not, apparently, fully consecrated and so is not capable of being used to celebrate weddings. However, early in 1989, the son of Mr Howland, the Chairman of the League of Friends of the Royal Sea Bathing Hospital, had his marriage, which had previously taken place in Canada, "Blessed" in the chapel and, on 30th July 1989 his son was baptised in it.

Chapter 5
THE CENTENARY

The year 1882 was memorable for another event very closely related to the Royal Sea Bathing Hospital, for it was in this year that Robert Koch discovered the tubercle bacillus. It is a sobering thought that the hospital had been specialising in the treatment of tuberculosis for almost a hundred years without knowing its cause!

It was also in that year that Pasteur produced his pioneering work of identifying micro-organisms, particularly the staphylococcus which had been and still is a major factor in human disease.

As always, the Visitors' Book continued to perform the job of giving a running commentary on the affairs of the hospital throughout the years. By 16th September 1882, Mr Edward Nicholls of Crouch End could write: "Much charmed with the whole building and particularly with the chapel". This was the first comment after the completion of the new Erasmus Wilson Wing and the chapel and they could only have been completed days before his visit.

In 1883 Lady Agnes Cooper wrote: "I can't find words to express my admiration for this place" (2nd April) and Rosa Blackwell was a patient then and recorded the fact when she visited the hospital in April 1923, some forty years later, another "long-term follow-up" (RSBHA 2.4.1883 and 1.4.1923). From time to time we get glimpses of other aspects of the hospital's work and it is recorded that the hospital chaplain was Rev. H. Aldwin Sames. There was a rather plaintive request from him that the chapel be "warmed".

Erasmus Wilson only survived the building of his huge extension by two years but, in his memory, a magnificent full-length statue of him was placed in the new front of the hospital. It was unveiled by Sir James Paget in 1896. He had been President of the Royal College of Surgeons six years before Erasmus and was responsible for describing, in 1876, "Paget's Disease of Bone", which is a common condition in orthopaedic practice, as well as certain other diseases.

One cannot omit, at this point, referring to the terms of Erasmus Wilson's will. After leaving various legacies, including another £5,000 to the Royal Sea Bathing Hospital, he left the residue to the Royal College of Surgeons. This proved to be no less a sum than £210,000 and was used to build the Hunterian Museum at the College (Cope, l.c.). Such a sum today could not be represented by a figure of less than £10,000,000. The museum

Institut Calot at Berck-Plage. A year younger than the Royal Sea Bathing Hospital, it serves the same purpose but is superbly maintained, equipped and staffed to the highest modern standards. The Royal Sea Bathing Hospital has been deliberately run down by the National Health Service and is now, alas, a sorry contrast.

lasted until 1941, when it was destroyed in a bombing raid on the night of 10th/11th May. The author himself studied in that museum and took part of the Fellowship Examination of the Royal College of Surgeons in the Hunterian Museum before the 1939-1945 war.

Mr Knight Treves who, with Mr Thornton, was surgeon to the hospital, gave an interview to a person using the pseudonym of "An Invalid". The latter wrote an article in the Daily Telegraph (2nd April 1885) entitled "Margate in Winter". After eulogising the Margate climate, he wrote: "The Royal Sea Bathing Infirmary was founded for the treatment of scrofula because Margate was the best place in England for the treatment of the disease" . . . "indeed, the results obtained are sometimes almost marvellous!" One of the patients who experienced this "marvellous" treatment and marvellous climate at the time was an F.C. Carter, while the Matron was Miss White. One of the sisters was known as "Kate" but it has not been possible to ascertain her surname. Clearly, however, she must have instilled great affection in all around her to come to be known by this familiar address at a time when the utmost formality was invariably observed.

An interesting publication in 1885 was entitled: *"De l'Influence des Bains de Mer sur la Scrofule des Enfants"* and it had a chapter on *"Infirmerie royale de Margate"*. This was written by Dr H. Cazin and comprised an extensive report on the Royal Sea Bathing Hospital in which he was helped by Dr Rowe. He reported that the Consultant Surgeon was Dr H. Curling and the Visiting Surgeons W.H. Thornton and W. Knight Treves. He seems to have made his visit in 1883, immediately after Erasmus Wilson's new

84

extensions were completed and describes the wards and sea bathing bath. He notes that the pump to fill the bath and also the pump for the central heating were gas fired. Dr Cazin's summary of his survey was: "... *l'Hospice de Margate, le plus ancien, est aussi le mieux ménage de tous ceux que j'ai vus*" (p.348). "... the Hospital at Margate, the oldest, and also the best institution of all those which I have seen." He was a member of the staff of *l'Hôpital Maritime de Berck-sur-mer* which later became the *Institut Calot*. This was the first connection established between the Royal Sea Bathing Hospital and the Institut Calot which is an Orthopaedic Hospital situated, like the Royal Sea Bathing Hospital, right on the very seaboard, but happily there have been many exchanges since. It has a great reputation and a Surgical and Medical Staff of the highest calibre. A very happy relationship in recent years has developed between the Royal Sea Bathing Hospital and the Institut Calot and a number of reciprocal visits have been arranged. The first visit to the Institut Calot was on 26th April 1974 and their return visit was on 24th October 1975. Details of subsequent visits will be found in chapter 14.

The subject of schooling repeatedly crops up during this story and it is reported that a Miss Pearce was appointed Governess by the Governors at a salary of £32 p.a. on 26th February 1885. This was not her first appearance, however, because prior to that time, but for how long is not certain, she had carried out the duties of Governess but her salary had been paid by a Mrs Warre.

Although anaesthetics originally came into use in the 1840s, the first reference to the use of chloroform in the Royal Sea Bathing Hospital that has been found in the records was in 1879 although it was not until 1884 that it came into regular use. Henley refers to being anaesthetised and the anaesthetic was almost certainly chloroform. However, this related to his experiences in Edinburgh and probably referred to the 1860s. At the same time, nitrous oxide was also being investigated at the hospital and in 1886 the Resident Surgeon applied for apparatus to produce anaesthesia by its use and the Directors approved of his indent and the apparatus was obtained (Resident Surgeon's Reports, MH/T1 M2 1, 1872-1889).

Two very fine gifts were received by the Royal Sea Bathing Hospital in 1886. The first, presented by Dr C.T. Richardson, was a leather-bound volume of Lettsom's Anniversary Oration to the Medical Society of London in 1778 with Lettsom's manuscript letter. The details have already been given (in chapter one) but it will be appreciated that these are among the most treasured possessions of the hospital.

The second was the magnificent gift of Charles A. Swinburne, who, on 20th December, offered £500 to procure a suitable organ, to be erected in the chapel, in memory of Erasmus Wilson's widow, the late Lady Wilson. This was, of course, accepted and Father Willis, one of the most famous organ-makers of the nineteenth century, was engaged to build it.

Mr W.T. Rees became the Resident Surgeon in 1887. He held the post for five years and was assisted for part of the time by his brother, as will be seen presently. On 30th May, Miss Collier retired. She had been Matron for over twenty years and was awarded a pension of £25 per annum. She was followed by Miss White but she retired after a very short time and was succeeded on 5th May 1888 by Miss Hilberry. There was a nurse at the hospital at that time by the name of Mercer. She later married James Dawkes and emigrated to Canada where she lived in Winnipeg, possibly an even windier location than Margate! (RSBHA 14, 24.4.1913).

It was the same year, on 23rd February 1888, that a letter was received by the Governors from the Visiting Surgeons which again recommended "that a properly fitted splint room . . . be provided" (KCC MH/T1 A8). Yet nothing seems to have been done until several years after Sir D'Arcy Power's similar suggestion in 1921!

The year 1888 was notable for a number of other memorable events. For example, on 27th September the Secretary of the High Wycombe Cottage Hospital was allowed the privileges of a Life Governor for a term, which was later fixed at ten years, on account of a donation from the hospital of ten guineas. This, of course, allowed the cottage hospital to nominate one patient a year for admission to the Royal Sea Bathing Hospital. In the same September, the South of England Telephone Company's offer to install a telephone line to the town was refused on account of the cost!

An interesting sidelight on how the English language was sometimes used in the nineteenth century is shown in the report of a visit, also on 5th May of the same year, of an ambulance class: ". . . an ambulance class for advanced nursing consisted of 17 Lady pupils visited the Infirmary this aft[n] and after rec[g] practical inst[n] in the wards as to bandaging — applic[n] of splints &c. they made inspection of the entire build[g]. They take this opport[y] of thanking the Matron (Miss Hilberry) for the kind arrangt[s] she made in respect of the Demonstra[n] and they would also record the great pleasure they have derived from inspecting the wards. T. Smith Rawes. St. John Ambulance Lecturer. Signed on behalf of the class, 5th May 1888".

On 7th August another remarkable visitation took place: the hospital was visited by Newton Jones and "300 friends"! Let us hope they made a very tangible contribution to the finances. (Unless, of course, it was a "flea circus"!)

The combination of the earlier discovery of anaesthetics and of antiseptics in the early 1870s meant that surgery in tuberculosis could be undertaken with increasing confidence. In the eleven months to 6th July 1888, operations under anaesthesia had been carried out 251 times, including excision or curettage of glands and amputations (Resident Surgeon's Reports, l.c., 1872-1889). In that report, of 463 patients reviewed, 414 were categorised as "cured, greatly benefitted or benefitted" and there were only seven deaths, six of which patients "being quite hopeless when they came down". Ada Longhurst was one of those who survived and returned to record her indebtedness thirty-four years later (RSBHA 14, 11.8.1922).

In 1889 the East Kent Branch of the British Medical Association visited the hospital and the doctors all signed the Visitors' Book. They were the forerunners of a great many visitors as members of various medical organisations from many countries, a service the hospital performs to this day in post-graduate education. Nor is this service limited to the medical profession. Many societies, such as physiotherapists, nursing tutors, pharmacists and others, have been welcome at the hospital for their meetings and to widen their experiences.

Many orthopaedic surgeons will be interested to learn that it was on 30th May 1889, over a hundred years ago, that it was decided that in future, all orders for surgical instruments should be placed with Messrs Down Brothers! (KCC MH/T1 A9).

The Royal Berkshire Hospital also became an Annual Governor on 29th June 1889 upon subscribing fifteen guineas annually to the Royal Sea Bathing Hospital. While the subscription of the Radcliffe Infirmary at Oxford was specifically to maintain a lien on a certain number of beds, the effect of becoming an Annual Governor was simply to hold the nomination of one patient for admission in any one year (ibid.).

On 8th December 1890, the Visiting Staff asked that an official application be made for a supply of Dr Koch's lymph for the cure of tuberculosis. This request was refused by the Court of Directors on the grounds that it "appears . . . to be somewhat premature in the present state of the discovery". However, by 23rd March 1891, Dr W.T. Rees, the Resident Surgeon, reported ten cases which had been treated with the lymph which he had somehow come by. They included four cases of lupus, three of true "scrofula", tuberculous glands of neck with sinuses, two of tuberculosis of the knee and one of the hip, all of which had multiple sinuses. From one to four injections of the "lymph" were given and although it was recognised that the treatment was too early to expect significant results, all were thought to have been markedly improved and, in some cases, sinuses were reported to have healed or appeared to be healing.

Dr J.L. Rees was appointed in 1890 as Assistant Surgeon to his brother and Registrar. At the same time, Lt.Col. Lewis Jones, Capt. G.A. Webb, Col. Elyard, Major Bell, R.E., Hon. Cecil Forester and Henry Hermitage, the Mayor of Margate, were all appointed to the Committee.

In this year a committee was set up to arrange the Centenary Celebrations for the following year. R. Ruthven Pym was treasurer and Thomas Dunn vice-president. Other members of the committee were P.S. Easton, H. Spencer Smith, C.A. Swinburne and Rev. Preb. Whittington, DD. Sadly, their deliberations did not reach quite the fruition hoped for, but more of that later.

It was well known that the proper treatment of patients with tuberculous conditions, and in particular, children, demanded a long stay in hospital. Ever since the schoolmaster who ". . . did not have to have a high standard of knowledge" was appointed in 1874, it seems that some sort of tuition was available either for the children or the convalescents. Again in 1891 a teacher was appointed and the school re-started. It had a chequered career and it seems that it was subsequently discontinued as it is reported that a school was "started" in 1914.

Reverting to the Centenary arrangements, the superintendent was to be a Mr J. Leger Burnett, who was to receive four per cent of the takings. This was changed to fifty guineas on 20th July, but later still was placed again at four per cent, but this time, however, only on those takings which he had been personally instrumental in attracting! One cannot help wondering what these changes really signified, particularly as the actual date of the Centenary had, by then, been passed! The members of the Executive Committee at Margate were also made members of the Centenary Committee but it seems to little avail.

One of the celebrations was to have taken the form of a Festival Dinner. Many prominent men were approached to preside at it but most of them refused for one reason or another. Clearly there was not, at that time, a member of any of the Committees who had Lettsom's almost universal contacts in the sphere of the wealthy, high-born or influential members of society! However, the Marquess of Lorne, Kt., PC, was eventually persuaded to accept. Alas, it seems as if all the arrangements fell through because no details have been found of any Festival Dinner in 1891. It does seem, however, that a belated dinner was held in the end, but not until 1895!

An important offer was made by Joseph Barton. He promised to donate the sum of £1,000 if four other persons could be found to give £250 each. Amongst others, this amount was donated by A.C. Swinburne, the Hon. Mrs Magniac and Charles Freeman. Obviously another donor put up the fourth contribution as Joseph Barton's £1,000 was paid in on 13th July 1891. A target of £50,000 had been mooted as an endowment but the sum eventually reached was very much less and may have been more nearly a tenth of that amount.

The Centenary Year, it will thus be seen, was not without its ups and downs.

In this year J.L. Rees, who had been assisting his brother, W.T. Rees, the Resident Surgeon, took over from him and was followed by Dr A.E. Thompson as Assistant Surgeon. But early in the new year, Thompson himself was succeeded by Edmund Kiewicz. A Miss A.G. Rees was a sister and one wonders if there was something of a family team taking a large part in the running of the hospital at that time.

Yet another hospital sought to have the right of nomination of a patient for admission to the Royal Sea Bathing Hospital and, on 14th December

1891, the Luton Cottage Hospital became an Annual Governor by making the appropriate annual subscription. It seems as if the figures quoted for the bed-strength of the hospital at various times were not altogether reliable. In 1892 it was claimed, apparently with some pride, that the hospital could now accept 220 patients at one time. But previous estimates had exceeded that number, so that precise figures are hard to come by. At least it gives us some indication of the approximate size of the hospital as the nineteenth century drew to its close.

On 18th September 1892 the hospital was visited by General James Pattison Walker. Another very important visitor in 1893 was the President of the Royal College of Physicians, Dr J. Russell Reynolds, and it is an indication of the reputation of the hospital that it continued to attract visits from the highest echelons of medicine.

Mrs Gardiner came down to Margate in the summer of 1913 (RSHBA 14) and reported that she had been a nurse at the hospital in 1893. However, she did not record her maiden name so no details of her service can be found.

Every major advance in Medicine in the nineteenth century helped the staff of the Royal Sea Bathing Hospital in their treatment of tuberculosis. Most prominent among these, though still twenty-five years after antiseptics and thirty-two years after Semmelweiss' paper on Prophylaxis of Puerperal Fever (de Kruif, 1933) was Faraboeuf's development of asepsis:

"Le chirurgien, honnête homme, est toujours
"aseptique et antiseptique. Aseptic, d'abord
"toujours de ne pas introduire lui-même dans
"le peau, avec les doigts, les instruments, le
"linge, l'eau . . . l'agent, le contage septique . . ."

"The surgeon, honest fellow, is always aseptic and antiseptic so as never himself to introduce into the wound with his fingers, the instruments, the swabs, the water . . . the agent, the septic contagion."

In this way, aseptic surgery was born and this again meant the most prodigious advance in the treatment of all surgical problems and, in particular, of tuberculosis. The avoidance of infection of a tuberculous lesion by a secondary organism was and is of absolutely paramount importance. In spite of the modern antibiotics, once a tuberculous focus has become secondarily infected, its chances of healing are very severely prejudiced.

Financial problems still continued to worry the administration and the various measures to improve the income of the hospital are seen in the Minute Book of the Fund-Raising Committee (RSBHA, 1893).

1894 is almost unique for one reason. It was the year that the only really adverse comment appeared in the Visitors' Book. On 15th August, Captain W.G. Pidduck, of Canterbury, wrote: "Did not go beyond the entrance hall. Decidedly prefer a clean, polished floor to a dirty Turkish carpet." In fact, this highlights a problem which is still with us. The perfect form of flooring for hospitals has still not been determined. While a "polished floor" may be most easily kept clean and most easily made surgically clean in, for instance, operating theatres, the best material from which to make it remains undiscovered. And the more polished a floor, the more slippery it is, a point that Captain Pidduck overlooked in a hospital treating lame and crippled patients.

We pass rapidly on to 1895 and now we find that a Festival Dinner was held. This was at the Metropole Hotel under the chairmanship of the Rt. Hon. Lord Chancellor, Lord Herschell. Also present on that rather belated occasion were:

Earl Stanhope	John Beaton
Sir Russell Reynolds, PRCP	E.L.S. Cocks
Sir Trevor Laurence, Bt.	John Croft
Sir Dyce Duckworth	Claude Baggallay
Sir Richard Wyatt	P.A. Easton
Rev. Preb. Whittington, DD	James Rankin, MP
MA, A Vice-President	Alan Gibbs
W. Howship Dickinson, MD	

The Lord Chancellor accepted the office of Vice-President of the charity.

The Festival Dinner at the Metropole Hotel raised a total of £1,152.3s.5d and as the expenses were £210.1s.0d there was a net profit of £942.2s.5d, a welcome addition to the funds.

This year the hospital was visited by Deputy Surgeon-General Sparrow, HMS, on 8th February and, on 28th March, by Mrs Gillison, LRCP&S (Ed), from Hankow, China. So we may assume that some of the expertise accumulated at the Royal Sea Bathing Hospital was in due course applied to the treatment of Chinese patients suffering from tuberculosis.

One of the most important of the resolutions of the Board of Directors was their decision, in June 1896, to recommend to the Governors that a new operating theatre should be built. It seems that there was considerable delay in implementing this resolution because it is recorded that the theatre was provided in 1905. At least, the outcome was the superb theatre which served so well for eighty years and became the cynosure of every surgeon who visited the hospital during that time. Some description of it will be found in a later chapter.

During the 1890s, correspondence was held with the London, Chatham and Dover Railway to try and persuade the company to allow reduced rail fares for directors and later for nurses and servants. It was ultimately agreed that the directors might have first class return railway fares between London and Margate for ten shillings and fifty such tickets were issued to the hospital for the use of named persons. Later, however, a concession was also made to extend the privileges of reduced third class fares to nurses and servants attached to the charity, ". . . even when travelling on their own business"! This agreement was finally reached, after a lot of correspondence, in April 1897 (KCC MH/T1 A9).

Miss Hilberry, who had been Matron since 1887, retired in 1895. There is a tablet in the chapel to her memory which gives her married name as Illington. It will be seen later that a Colonel Illington, IMS, visited the hospital in 1919 and it seems possible that she retired to marry as he had previously been one of the Resident Surgeons. She died in 1939.

Edmund Kiewicz relinquished the post of Assistant Resident Surgeon in 1895 and was replaced by Orwin Shields, who served for eighteen months.

Another epoch-making discovery came to light in 1895. This was the achievement of Wilhelm Konrad Roentgen in describing the X-ray and its application to the examination of bones and joints of the human body. Radiography has since been of inestimable benefit in diagnosis in every field of medicine, none more so than in that of bone and joint tuberculosis.

In 1896 the residual legacy of Mary Ann Carlton matured from which the Royal Sea Bathing Hospital benefited to the tune of rather over £5,000. One of the clauses governing the will was that the Vicar of Fulham should have three nominations for admission. Carlton Ward was thus named in her memory.

Another important milestone in the history of the Royal Sea Bathing Hospital occurred on 28th March 1898, when Queen Victoria approved the change of name of the hospital from the Royal Sea Bathing Infirmary, as it had been known since the Prince of Wales first gave it his patronage in 1791, to the Royal Sea Bathing Hospital. It must have been subsequent to that date, therefore, that the name now seen over the entrance to the hospital was placed there.

It was also at this time that the purpose of the hospital was officially and explicitly expanded although the interpretation of its original purpose, as we have seen, was already elastic. It was resolved ". . . that the purpose for which this charity is established be defined as 'For the reception of patients suffering from tuberculosis and other diseases which . . . require the benefits of sea air and sea bathing for their successful treatment'" (ibid). No such resolution was made, unless it was made in the fastnesses of the South East Metropolitan Regional Hospital Board in Croydon, when the scope of the service the hospital was to render was again expanded in the early 1950s and gradually over the subsequent decades!

As has already been mentioned, it was in 1896 that Sir James Paget came down to Margate and unveiled the magnificent statue of Erasmus Wilson in the forecourt of the hospital, standing facing the wing built through his philanthropy and munificence. The statue was presented to the hospital but the name of the donor was not revealed.

"In August 1896 my brother was operated on here, twenty-three years ago, with great success and I consider the present management excellent," wrote Ernest Appleton, who visited the hospital in 1919 accompanied by Fanny Appleton of Chicago, USA. It was in 1897 that Selina Taylor was a patient in the hospital. Again a grateful patient returned to the hospital twenty-five years later and demonstrated that her treatment had been permanently successful (RSBHA 14, 11.8.1922). There can be relatively few occasions nowadays when such loyalty is shown by people travelling great distances to visit a hospital where they had been treated twenty or thirty years before.

At this time Dr Bertram Thornton was Visiting Surgeon at the hospital, as his father had been before him, and he served until 1913. It was his daughter, Mrs Phyllis Cobb, who remembered, as a girl, accompanying him on his rounds at the hospital, as already described in chapter 3. Another well-known visitor who signed the Visitors' Book in 1897 was the Rev. Prebendary Webb-Peploe. He was one of the foremost evangelical preachers of the early part of the twentieth century.

In 1898 there followed in rather quick succession Drs Woodman, Heston and McAnelly as Resident Assistant Surgeons. Raistrick (l.c. 1898) reported that the hospital now had 300 beds, but this must have included many balcony beds in the count. Following Dr McAnelly, Dr Edmund Hall became Assistant Resident Surgeon before the year was out.

On 13th September 1899 the hospital received a visit from Mrs J.L. Edlmann. She was the great-granddaughter of John Coakley Lettsom and was accompanied by her daughter, Caroline Eliot Edlmann who was therefore his great-great-granddaughter, as was Edith Edlmann who visited the hospital five days later. So Lettsom's descendants continued to maintain the family interest in the hospital he had founded over a hundred years previously.

Charles Harnett succeeded to the post of Resident Surgeon in this year and he was assisted by Howard Gresham. He was appointed Visiting Surgeon in 1905 but died the following year. One wonders if again the cause was the tubercle bacillus, caught in the line of duty.

To round off the nineteenth century, a garden party was held at the Royal Sea Bathing Hospital. It was attended by at least 128 people who signed the Visitors' Book but one of these signed his name and appended: "and party", so that it is impossible to be exact as to the actual number. Together with staff, there must have been in the region of 150 people enjoying what we hope was a fine afternoon on the lawns of the hospital.

Three important additions to the hospital funds were received in the last few years of the nineteenth century: Walter Swinburne gave £20,000 in 1892 and, in 1898, the Archbishop of Canterbury, Dr Temple, appropriated £3,600 to the hospital's endowment fund under the will of the late Alfred Marriott of Hopton. Finally, in 1899, the hospital received a legacy of £5,000 under the will of General John Julius Johnstone. It was in such ways as this that the Voluntary Hospitals managed to keep financially afloat until the taxation of the late 1930s in preparation for the Second World War made such generosity impossible.

Chapter 6

THE START OF THE TWENTIETH CENTURY

The year and the twentieth century opened with the generous presentation to the Royal Sea Bathing Hospital, by Caroline Eliot Edlmann, of a fine print of the Medley Picture, the original of which hangs in the Medical Society of London's Headquarters, Lettsom House. The print hangs in the Committee Room of the hospital and shows John Coakley Lettsom presenting the keys of his house at Bolt Court, in the City of London, to the Society which he founded in 1773. The Society met there for many years.

Harry Dodgson was the Resident Surgeon and we have the names of three other people who appear to have had a dual rôle. James Penny, aged nineteen, was a scullery boy and Florence Austin and Rhoda Reed were wardmaids on Alexandra Ward. But it seems that they were, at the same time, patients as well. Just how the two capacities were combined is not known, though it may be opined that this was an early form of occupational therapy or rehabilitation.

It does not seem, however, that any really organised form of occupational therapy or what might be called active rehabilitation was developed for many years, not, at least, until after the Second World War.

Another remarkable occasion occurred on 18th March 1901. It was on this day that it is recorded that "His Majesty the King gladly accords his patronage to the Royal Sea Bathing Hospital". This means that King Edward VII not only gave his patronage within two months of his accession to the throne but held a very different approach to the question from that of his grandson when he became King Edward VIII, which is dealt with in a later chapter, but which was exactly the reverse of that of his grandfather.

Throughout the history of the hospital up to now, there must have been remarkably little inflation. In this year, 1901, the pay for staff nurses was still only £25 per annum. This still represents no increase in the rate as compared with 1853, when it was ten shillings a week, or £26 a year. Not only so, but the rate for nurses in any case remained abysmal, that for first year probationers at St Bartholomew's Hospital, London, in 1932 still being only £25 per annum!

An important agreement was reached on 11th April 1900 between the Royal Sea Bathing Hospital and the Corporation of Margate. The Corporation wished to build a sea wall and promenade between the hospital and the beach, so integral a part of the hospital's function, both for sea-bathing and for the child patients who were encouraged to play on the sands.

93

The agreement confirmed ". . . the right of the hospital to have access across the promenade to the shore with or without wheeled vehicles, including bathing machines, and the right of the hospital patients and inmates to bathe in a reasonable and proper manner from machines and tents on the beach in front of their property".

Appropriate access from the hospital to the shore was promised and also preservation of the intake and supply of sea water to be secured, the Corporation agreeing to lengthen the intake to secure a proper supply of pure and clean water (C & T DHA Doc.6).

It seems, therefore, that the hospital was still extracting water from the sea for treatment purposes and was continuing to pump it up to the baths which were still actively in use.

In the present century, records are much fuller but they are still very incomplete. Amongst other causes is the fact that the main minutes of the Directors of the charity were kept in London and were lost in air raids during the Second World War. Also, alas, some of those stored at the Royal Sea Bathing Hospital were lost on account of being so badly damaged by water from a burst water tank that many of them are largely indecipherable, even where the paper has not actually disintegrated (see colour plate).

A separate list of various office holders is in existence but it would be tedious to include them all in the narrative, particularly as there are now so many names recorded. However, this will not preclude the mention of many of them where there is a special reason for doing so and it may be observed that the Superintendent this year was a Commander Gray, RN, the Matron was Mrs Hannay and the Secretary was another Mr Nash. He served for thirty-six years in this capacity. It seems that the Navy has a special place in the medical services of Thanet because, since his appointment in 1985, the District General Manager of the Canterbury and Thanet District Health Authority, within which administration the Royal Sea Bathing Hospital now lies, has been Vice-Admiral Sir John Cadell, KBE (RN Retired). However, the Army was always very well represented: the minutes of the Court of Directors, No.111, for 31st December 1901 may be taken as an example of the full administrative set up of the hospital in those days and it will be seen to include many Army officers:

Patron	HM King Edward VII.
Vice-Patrons	HRH the Duke of Cambridge and the Rt. Hon. the Lord Archbishop of Canterbury.
President	The Earl of Derby, KG.
Vice-Presidents	The Earls of Jersey, Stanhope & Halsbury, Viscount Clifton, Lord Grimthorpe, The Very Rev. the Dean of Ripon, the Rt. Hon. the Lord Mayor of London, Charles S. Hardy, C.A. Swinburne and Henry Weigall.
Treasurer	Martin Biddulph.

Martin Biddulph was created a Baron in 1903 and was owner, or part owner, of Cocks and Biddulph's Bank, at 16 Whitehall. He maintained the account of the Royal Sea Bathing Hospital at this bank, and his son and grandson followed him. The latter, with the Hon. Thomas Egerton, eventually passed the bank on to Martin's Bank and, quite recently, this became Barclays. The account was terminated, of course, when the National Health Service took over.

The Court of Directors consisted of H.A. Bentinck, Major General F.L. Campbell, A.B. Cobb, John Croft, W. Howship Dickinson, MD, Major Elliott, Rt. Hon. Lord Forester, Colonel Isacke, late RA, Sir Trevor Laurence, Bt., Sir Henry F. Lennard, Bt., Hector W.G. MacKenzie, MD, Major Milner, F.C. Norton, Newton C. Ogle, Alfred Willett and Hon. A. Yorke.

Trustees: Martin Biddulph, Lord Forester and Captain G.A. Webbe.

Ex-officio were the Hon. Visiting Surgeons Bertram Thornton, Arthur Rowe and W. Greenwood Sutcliffe, the Hon. Consulting Surgeons Thomas S. Rowe and W. Knight Treves and the Hon. Assistant Visiting Surgeon C.J. Harnett.

The Chaplain was Rev. A.D. Cope and the Superintendent Commander Gray. Mrs Hannay was the Matron and she became Matron-Superintendent when Commander Gray left in 1903 and remained in the post until 1914. As mentioned above, A. Nash was Hospital Secretary and served until 1936.

The names of the London Medical Board will be known to many medical readers, they included the Physicians T. Barlow, T.H. Green, W. Cayley, F.D. Havilland Hill, W.B. Cheadle, Stephen MacKenzie, W.H. Dickinson, P.H. Pye Smith, Sir Dyce Duckworth, Sir Edward Sieveking and David Ferrier.

The Surgeons of the London Medical Board were Stanley Boyd, (Sir) H.G. Howse (this designation will represent those who were subsequently honoured), John Croft, Jonathan Hutchinson, (Sir) R.J. Godlee, Rt. Hon. Lord Lister, A. Pearce Gould, Edmund Owen, J. Warrington Howard, Alfred Willett and Luther Holden.

The hospital also had another visit from Sir Frederick Treves who, it will be remembered, had worked in the hospital in 1876. He retained an abiding interest in the Royal Sea Bathing Hospital and paid several visits to it over the years.

The total number of patients admitted in the whole year was 651 and the average bed occupancy 119. This would suggest an average stay of only two months, which is highly unlikely. So, as usual, we must doubt the accuracy of some of these figures because, with Erasmus Wilson's four large wards, all with balconies, the bed strength should have been well over 200, which would have allowed an average stay of nearly four months. Some reports suggest a figure of rather more in the region of 300.

95

Christmas in the wards, 1903.

Rose Gilbert was a patient in 1901 when, at the age of six, she was treated for tuberculous glands of the neck . . . scrofula! Sixty-two years later she returned, as Mrs Alsopp, and donated ten shillings in appreciation of her treatment.

Amongst the patients treated in the hospital in 1903 was a child from the Royal Estate at Sandringham. In token of his appreciation of the treatment that the child received, HM King Edward VII made a donation of thirty guineas, a fact that the Court of Directors records as entitling His Majesty to become a Life Governor of the charity! That such a person should be a patient in the Royal Sea Bathing Hospital is an indication of the fact that its increasing reputation led to applications for treatment being received from all over the country and it was a truly national institution until the advent of the National Health Service.

It has already been noted that, as early as 1823, the hospital was receiving patients from Oxford and in 1859 it was said that patients from sixteen counties occupied a third of the 250 beds (Dover Express and Intelligencer, July 1859).

While it is, as has been remarked, of great interest to read of those who owed a debt to the hospital, it is also of equal interest and importance to learn more of those to whom the hospital is indebted. Foremost among these are the nurses. Clara Elizabeth Robson was a nurse in the hospital in

1901. She lived to be ninety and died in 1961. At the same time, Nurse Gillett was working in the hospital under Mrs Hannay. We shall certainly hear more about the nurses as time goes on.

1901 saw the first appointment of a theatre sister. We do not know her name but she was assisted by two staff nurses.

Some of the entries are indecipherable, as has been remarked, but some are otherwise unusual. This year saw two patients apparently suffering from "Obitis", a disease not known to the present generation of medicals! The only alternative explanation is that it is intended to be a cryptic way of saying that they died.

It may have been that it was the turn of the century that triggered off inflation because, on 28th April 1902 there was a further increase in the amount patients had to pay. Originally between four and six shillings a week was considered to be a realistic figure to be charged a patient and that changed little over the nineteenth century. Now, however, the full rate was no less than thirty shillings a week with an "ordinary" rate of twelve shillings for an adult and eight shillings for a child.

Of course, the hospital still depended very largely on the voluntary support which it had enjoyed since its inception and was to continue to enjoy right up until the Second World War. People still contributed generously to charities of all descriptions, as they have done in Britain in remarkable ways in the face of national and international disasters as well as to domestic charities. So it was that, on 26th May 1903, Mrs Matthews donated £1,000, still an enormous figure in those days, representing considerably more than a very well off person could expect to earn in a year. Another very helpful legacy was received the following year under the will of the late Baron de Rothschild of £1,120.

"Every clergyman . . . who may have preached a sermon or have given his pulpit or collected an offertory in favour of the charity, whereby a sum of not less than two guineas shall have been collected, shall, during the ensuing twelve months, be entitled to one ordinary letter for every complete sum of two guineas so collected. If the offertory amount to ten guineas or upwards, he shall be entitled to the privileges of a quinquenniel Governor" (RSBHA 160, p.67). (A "letter" was a letter of recommendation of a patient for in-patient treatment.)

In 1902 we read of the first appointment of an Honorary Dental Surgeon who was Mr F.H. Bailey King. One of the Vice-Patrons, the Archbishop of Canterbury, Dr Temple, died in this year. Another death was that of Nurse Fannie Matilda Pell, who died while in the service of the hospital on 13th June. She may also have been a victim of the occupational hazard of contracting tuberculosis which was then, and still is in many parts of the world, a crippling and a killing disease.

C.A. Swinburne, the Treasurer and much venerated benefactor of the hospital, died in 1903. A ward was named in his honour. He died just before

C.A. Swinburne

he was due to take the chair at a meeting of the Directors at the end of the year. Swinburne Ward was used right up until the Second World War. It remained vacant for a number of years after the war and was used as a store, but in the 1980s it was converted into a very much overdue post-operative recovery ward. Under the terms of Swinburne's will, some £12,500 was transferred to the hospital and a mortgage of £25,000.

The President, Lord Derby, gave £1,000 to endow a bed in the hospital for the free treatment of a patient.

Another interesting addition to the hospital's assets came from the F.R. Simmond's Trust, whereby a cottage and fifty-nine acres at St Nicholas-at-Wade were presented to the hospital. Subsequent offers for the land reached £70 per acre but were declined. The property was rented at £50 per acre originally but this was raised to £75 in 1918. The income was divided between the Royal Sea Bathing Hospital and the Kent & Canterbury Hospital.

In the context of ward names, it must be remarked that a ward was named after Lettsom, as may be imagined. It subsequently became the first ward to admit male patients for orthopaedic conditions of a non-tuberculous nature and later was converted into a Physiotherapy Department. The development of Physical Medicine was a feature of this period. It first arose out of the Danish invention of the Finsen Light for the treatment of lupus, a tuberculous affection of the skin, and which was one of the first aspects of "Medical Electricity" to attract specialised attention. It was in the year 1904 that a Dr Charles Heston, MD, was appointed to the staff as Honorary Surgeon to the "Electricity Department", and a fund was started to provide "an X-ray machine *(sic)* for the treatment of lupus". Whether

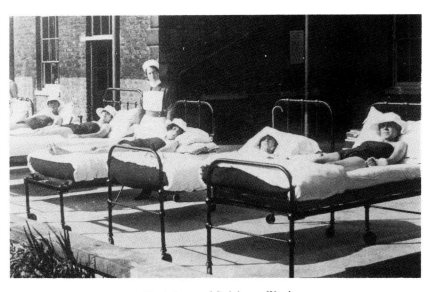

The balcony of Swinburne Ward.

this was simply a lay misnomer for a Finsen Light is not certain but we have no definite knowledge that the hospital ever did possess a Finsen Light which was a variety of ultra-violet light.

"The History of The London Hospital" (Morris, 1910) records that the Finsen Light Department there was a very expensive department to run. The adoption of Finsen treatment at that hospital was initiated by the Consort of King Edward VII, our Patron, no less a person that HM Queen Alexandra, when she was Princess of Wales, and therefore prior to 1901.

The Hatfeild family were considerable land-owners in Westbrook and the name "Taddy" appears as a Christian name in some members of the Hatfeild family which suggests that there may have been a family connection. There is, of course, a ward named Hatfeild Ward in the General Hospital at Margate.

There are conveyances of several parcels of property from the Hatfeilds to the Trustees of the Royal Sea Bathing Hospital at different times from 1872 onwards. These included a large area behind the "Dog and Duck" public house, extending to the sea and to Westbrook Gardens and also two houses in Westbrook Terrace. This last was completed in 1881 in the sum of £400 (C & T DHA Doc.4).

The property of the Royal Sea Bathing Hospital became vested in the Official Trustee of Charity Lands by order of the Charity Commission in 1919 (C & T DHA Doc.16, 1507/19, A/37, 326). It was they that sanctioned

50 years' nursing service recognised

A LIFETIME'S service with the nursing profession was recognised by the Shrewsbury Group Hospital Management Committee on Feb. 27 when a plaque was unveiled at the Royal Salop Infirmary to commemorate the 50 years' service which Miss Alice Elizabeth Hicks had completed.

The plaque — in the women's surgical ward where Miss Hicks had been sister for about 10 years— was unveiled by the chairman of the Group Hospital Management Committee, Mr. Lewis Motley. Miss Hicks was present at the ceremony with her brother, and there were also members of the Management Committee, the matron and other nurses present.

Miss Hicks, awarded the M.B.E. last year, now aged 71 and living at Burford, Oxford, retired from the R.S.I. in October, 1956, after 50 years in nursing. She started her career at a Margate hospital and received her training there and at the Royal Infirmary, Worcester. She subsequently held appointments at the City Hospital, Worcester, again at the Royal Infirmary, Worcester, and at the Huddersfield Royal Infirmary, where she remained for five or six years, before becoming surgical sister (women) at the R.S.I. in 1929. She was night superintendent at the hospital from March, 1939. Miss Hicks was vice-president of the local Nurses' League.

STAFF NURSE IN THE THEATRE.
R.S.B.H. (1909) - MISS ALICE HICKS.
MISS ALICE HICKS. S.R.N. STARTED HER
TRAINING AT THE ROYAL SEA BATHING
HOSPITAL, & FINISHED IT AT ROYAL INFIRMARY
WORCESTER.

PROBATIONER ALICE HICKS ON MAUDE
BACONY. CHAPEL DOOR ARE BOTH OPEN

The story of Alice Hicks.

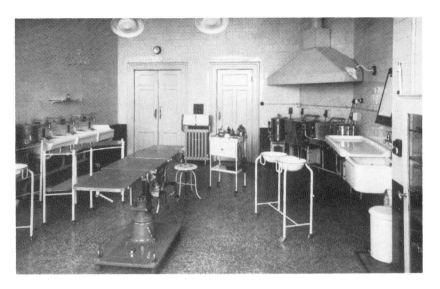

The Operating Theatre. Note the steam sterilizers in the corner.

the sale of Nos. 56 and 58 Westbrook Terrace for something over £5,000 which went towards payment for the new King George V wards in 1919.

An epidemic of "nasal diphtheria" affected the patients in the hospital in 1905 but was said to occur "intermittently"! In spite of the serious nature of diphtheria, no very great alarm seems to have been caused by this epidemic and it must have been a curiously innocuous organism that was involved.

One of the most important improvements that took shape this year was "a spacious operating theatre". This was a magnificent theatre with far more room than is provided in operating theatres today. Some comments will be made upon it later but the most remarkable feature of it was the huge north-facing window which gave directly onto the beach and the North Sea.

Comparison of the various costs involved in running a hospital continue to make remarkable reading and, in 1905, the average overall cost per occupied bed per week was £1.7s.1d, or a little over £70 a year.

Dr Harnett was appointed as Visiting Surgeon in 1905 but died before the year was out and Dr Duncan, who had been Assistant Resident Surgeon in 1904, was promoted to the senior post though he only held it for a short time, being followed by Dr Coullie.

A fascinating story begins in 1906. In that year, there was a probationer starting her training in the hospital named Alice Elizabeth Hicks. The illustration shows her as the farther of the two nurses on the balcony of Maud Ward. (The chapel doors are both open so that daylight can be seen through the chapel at the far end of the balcony.) Alice Hicks duly qualified and the

101

St Luke's Hospital, Lowestoft.

second picture shows her when she was operating theatre staff nurse here in 1909. She finally appears in 1956, when she retired with the rank of Sister from the Royal Salop Infirmary after having devoted fifty years of her life to nursing, a period of active service which had begun at the Royal Sea Bathing Hospital.

£1,000 was still a very large sum indeed in the early years of the century and Mrs Hannah Finnie's legacy of £1,000 to endow a bed was a very tangible contribution to the hospital's finances.

At this time the Medical Board advised against the admission of patients suffering from pulmonary tuberculosis, that is, tuberculous infection of the lungs. This recommendation was made on the grounds that "cases of Pulmonary Consumption do not make satisfactory progress during their residence here". The Margate air was deemed "too strong" for such delicate chests. However, the idea is not altogether fanciful because at St Luke's Hospital, Lowestoft, the same philosophy obtained in the late 1930s.

St Luke's Hospital was in many ways very comparable with the Royal Sea Bathing Hospital. It was not a Voluntary Hospital, being the London County Council's adult surgical tuberculosis sanatorium, but it catered for exactly the same category of patient, excepting the children. It was situated in a very similar manner to the Royal Sea Bathing Hospital, in that it was right on the top of the cliff overlooking the North Sea and facing due east

102

and so was exposed to the same north and north-east winds that prevail in Margate. Alas, St Luke's Hospital is no more. It was demolished after the war, during which it had served as a naval headquarters.

In 1907 the 220 beds in use at the Royal Sea Bathing Hospital were reviewed in the light of "modern ideas of hygiene". In consequence, it was thought that the hospital was too crowded and therefore the establishment was reduced to 150 beds. Perhaps this was the flint that struck the spark to enlarge the hospital again, a project that was to be interrupted by the Great War, though it came to fruition soon after it.

George Judkins was a patient about this time and returned, as so many of them did, to visit the scene of his cure sixteen years later, on 30th March 1923. Mentioning the recurrence of this type of occasion so often is not done without reason. The Royal Sea Bathing Hospital has been, throughout the years, not only a source of excellence but an organisation where the care of the patient and the happiness of the staff have always occupied pride of place. Its principle is that the most important person in the hospital is the patient. The result is a loyalty to the hospital of all concerned which is outstanding and which, in spite of all the buffetings that have arisen under the National Health Service, remains undiminished.

In 1908 HSH Prince Alexander of Teck became President of the Hospital and took a very personal interest in its progress. He was to become the Earl of Athlone and will be referred to under that name in this history. He married HRH Princess Alice who became the Countess of Athlone. They both gave most generous service to the hospital.

Miss J.A. Tomkin was the Sister of Alexandra Ward and had as her Staff Nurse E.E. Smeeton. One of the nurses was E. Florence Dawkes, a probationer, but no more is known of her.

This year saw the death of W. Knight Treves who had served the hospital for so long. Dr Bertram Thornton retired this year, but continued as Visiting Surgeon until 1913. Two surgeons followed their fathers' footsteps in the service of the Royal Sea Bathing Hospital, first the Thorntons and now the Treves, for Frederick Boileau Treves, son of W. Knight Treves, was appointed as Assistant Visiting Surgeon in 1910 when the then Assistant Surgeon, Dr J.L. Sawyers was promoted to the senior post.

A remarkable step forward was taken in 1910 when electricity was installed throughout the hospital in lieu of the previous gas lighting. Electric lighting was installed at the same time at the London Hospital (Morris, l.c.), which shows that the Royal Sea Bathing Hospital was not lagging in adopting modern methods. However, emergency lighting continued to be by gas.

On his accession to the throne in 1910, HM King George V immediately renewed the Royal Patronage, so continuing the unbroken history of royal interest in the hospital. Sadly, his son was to break the tradition twenty-six years later.

In this year it was reported that "the old swimming bath, which is not now required, has been converted into an exellent ward containing fourteen beds with large and pleasant day rooms on the first floor which are approached by a staircase of easy gradient" (RSBHA 172, p.8). No explanation was offered as to why the swimming bath was no longer required. It seems that this really saw the end of actual "sea bathing" in the treatment of the patients at the hospital. At least, "Sea-water Russell's" ideas of the value of sea bathing had lasted for 160 years and Lettsom's espousal of the method had created a hospital of no little importance in medical history.

While the sea-water swimming baths were discontinued, work was completed on providing balconies on the west side of the wards of the Wilson Wing, for Maud, Victoria, Louise and Alexandra. These were wide balconies, parts of which were covered and parts left open to the sky. At least Lettsom's idea of solaria was continued and patients spent most or sometimes all of their time exposed to the elements. The cost of this addition, which was completed in 1909, was £537.

Sir Humphrey Rolleston, Sir D'Arcy Power and Sir J. Galloway, though not yet knighted, and also Sir Frederick Eve were members of the London Medical Board at this time and became leaders of the profession in the next two decades, maintaining the tradition of the highest possible standards in the medical supervision of the charity. At the same time, Sir Jonathan Hutchinson, another of the giants of the profession, left the Board.

Dr Arthur Rowe had been Local Surgeon to the Royal Sea Bathing Hospital for many years, having taken up practice in Margate in the middle 1880s. He was a First Class Graduate of Durham University and served the hospital until his retirement in 1910, when he built a superb villa in Shottendane Road, now a beautiful nursing home. He was a successful and well-liked practitioner and achieved great fame as an archaeologist and palaeontologist, so following in the steps of Erasmus Wilson! He died in 1926 at the age of eighty-eight (I.o.T. Gazette).

One of the visitors to the hospital in 1911 was Mr C.A. Mount, late Captain, "The Buffs". He was said to be the nephew of Mr William Oliver Chalk, who had been Resident Surgeon at the hospital from 1820-1845 (RSBHA 14). (One would have thought that he might have been a great-nephew, in view of the long time interval, but perhaps it was possible.) The name of Mount was widely known in East Kent for many years, and particularly during the middle years of the twentieth century. Many of the family held Commissions in "The Buffs", the Royal Artillery and other arms of the Services and fought in the Second World War. They were extensive farmers, fruit, rose and carnation growers and were founder-members of the national fruit growing, storing and distributing firm of "Home Grown Fruits". One of the most prominent members of the family, Mr "Jim" Mount, was knighted in 1979.

It was in 1911 that Miss Kempson was appointed Assistant Matron on the recommendation of the Matron of St George's Hospital. She followed Miss Bickham who retired.

Mention of this appointment brings to mind some of the regulations in force at that time for nurses. Discipline is a word which is not understood today but, in the years preceding the First World War, it was a very real thing. The following are extracts from the "Rules and Regulations" for 1911 which, we may be sure, were very much respected.

Nurses. Day Duty

Rise 6 a.m. Breakfast 6.40 a.m. Wards 7 a.m. Lunch 10 a.m. Dinner 12.30 p.m. Tea 4.30 p.m. Supper 8 or 8.30 p.m. Lights out 10.30 p.m. Off Duty: 2 hours daily, 10-12, 2-4 or 5-7.

Staff Nurses

One evening each week, from 5-10 p.m.
Every second Sunday, from 4.30-10 p.m.
One day off duty every month.
One afternoon a week, from 2-5 p.m.

Probationers

Every second Sunday from 5 till 8.30 p.m.
One day off duty every two months.
One week and one fortnight every year.
One afternoon a week from 2-5 p.m.

How many nurses would be kept today with off-duty of that description?

1911 saw the introduction of Lloyd-George's National Insurance Act. Under Section 16(1)(a) of the Act, the Royal Sea Bathing Hospital was recognised and apparently some improvements were undertaken, but what these were is not known.

Two contributions were received at this time, both of £1,000, which was still a very large amount. One was under the will of Joseph Barton and the other from one of the Vice-Presidents, Mrs Streatfield, who endowed the Henry John bed. The same sum was received the following year under the will of Mr Mappin.

Mrs Hannay retired from the post of Matron in 1913 and was granted a pension of £75 p.a. This was probably not riches but £100 p.a. was a not uncommon income amongst the ranks of the lower paid before the Great War. At this time, the average cost for an occupied bed for a year was £69.17s.6d. With the inclusion of all overheads, this perhaps throws some light on the value of Mrs Hannay's pension.

Mrs Hannay was followed by Miss Kempson as Matron-Superintendent, who was later awarded the RRC and served until her death in October 1923.

Signature of HSH Alexander of Teck, 5th June 1913.

The Board recorded (RSBHA 175) that "the effort which has been made to insure some measure of education for children of school age in the Institution appears very creditable as a good beginning and the Board hopes that this may be further developed, together with the practice of wood-carving or other manual work, for many of the adult patients." The school had originally been started in 1874, but must have been discontinued at various times because it was re-opened in April 1914, the Mistress being Mrs Hilda Mahoney, and continued until 1917. The usual school subjects were taught but, in addition, brush-work and rug-making for the boys and fancy work and blouse-making for the girls. Cane weaving was introduced for the older scholars. The fancy work and rugs fetched £2.3s.5d and so the project was self-financing. A clear indication emerges of the institution of occupational therapy in the hospital, surely a very far-seeing, if not a completely pioneering, achievement! It would be interesting to discover if such a forward step had previously been adopted at any other hospital.

Two patients were in the hospital in the immediate pre-war days and subsequently returned to visit the hospital, as seems to have been such a regular occurrence. C.C. Ball returned in 1919 and S. Brittain in September 1927, the latter to report that he was "perfectly well". Another interesting visitor came in 1913 to enter in the Visitors' Book: "Patient in this hospital over forty years ago and again thirty years ago. I find there are great improvements." This was Henry O. Groves who had, by now, become Archdeacon of London and Domestic Chaplain to Queen Alexandra.

Prince Alexander of Teck paid another of his visits to the hospital in his rôle of President and signed the Visitors' Book on 5th June 1913. During the war soon to develop, he was created the Earl of Athlone.

Less than a month before the outbreak of war, the famous surgeon, Sir D'Arcy Power, came down to Margate to see for himself the hospital for which he had already served for some four years as a member of the London Medical Board.

Within a month, World War had begun.

106

Chapter 7

THE FIRST WORLD WAR
AND BASIL ARMSTRONG

While the lady who was to become Mrs Miller lay in the Royal Sea Bathing Hospital suffering from tuberculosis of the spine and a psoas abscess in the groin, the country was precipitated into the World War, the War to end War! Naturally the Royal Sea Bathing Hospital opened its doors to the wounded, though it continued to treat the scrofulous poor. Some of the first patients to be admitted after the start of the war were fifty-three Belgian soldiers who arrived on 14th October 1914. Many of them were, apart from their wounds, in a most destitute condition. This was quickly remedied by local friends, the British Red Cross Society and the Belgian Relief Fund.

At the same time British soldiers were admitted also, in all some 115 soldiers from the Battle of Mons came into the Royal Sea Bathing Hospital before the end of 1914.

For many years there had been two Resident Surgeons at the Royal Sea Bathing Hospital, one of whom, at this time, was Joseph Hodnutt and he and his colleagues had to step up their activities greatly to handle this influx of what will have comprised some very major and complicated injuries. But the country could not spare doctors for civilian life, at least, not male doctors, and so it was that, in 1915, the first lady doctor was appointed to a resident post at the Royal Sea Bathing Hospital in the person of Miss E.M. Hall, LMSSA. Mr Sutcliffe and Mr Treves were away on military service and Doctors Heaton and Sawers had to undertake much extra work.

It was possible, however, for some civilian work to go on and so we read of ward balconies being widened and children's accommodation being increased. Fifty beds were put aside for soldiers and 153 were admitted during 1915. Those discharged from the Services suffering from tuberculosis continued to be treated, as were some wounded and also some suffering from shell-shock.

There must have been many new problems arising in the treatment of conditions often so different from the tuberculous lesions that the hospital was accustomed to handle. Not least of these may have been the fact that, as the hospital was on the coast nearly opposite the battle-fronts, a degree of blackout was imposed for which there were not the preparations nor the facilities that were commonplace in 1939. In addition, both nursing and domestic help were in short supply and we may imagine the difficulties that had to be overcome in spite of everything.

A rather unexpected source of funds is reported at this time in that, amongst others who supported the hospital, finance was forthcoming from the Governments of Queensland and New Brunswick and the Trinidad Planters. Exactly how this came about is not certain.

The happy association which had begun many years previously was continued in 1917 with further visits from the Earl of Athlone and Princess Alice. The frequent visits that he and the Princess made continued even after he became Governor General of Canada in 1939 and after the Second World War. As far as the Royal Sea Bathing Hospital was concerned, the Presidency was not looked upon as a sinecure and no hospital could have been happier with its royal connections.

The same year saw J.F. Hutchins a patient in the hospital. He made good progress and returned in 1923 to express his appreciation, so endorsing the recognised pattern!

Another remarkable example of the interest that the Royal Family always took in the Royal Sea Bathing Hospital was the donation, in 1917, of £200 to the hospital by HM Queen Alexandra. Some gifts in kind were also received, for Sir Ernest Cassell sent game and Lord Biddulph, the Treasurer at that time, venison. As was almost universal in the Second World War, some "Dig for Victory" activities were developed and part of the hospital grounds were dug up to grow vegetables.

In spite of the war, the school extended its activities and an assistant teacher was appointed and the education extended to some of the children who were still confined to their beds. For the girls, subjects now included plain and fancy needlework, knitting, raffia canvas work, raffia weaving, Indian basketry and drawing. For the boys some of the same subjects were encouraged, such as drawing, raffia winding, raffia weaving, Indian basketry and English. They were also taught English basketry, flower making and plasticine modelling. Again, the cost of such developments was met, in whole or in part, by sales which, this year, reached £5.0s.8d.

The Report of the Court of Directors in 1918 contains the following paragraph:

"Recent legislation has made it practically impossible for Special Hospitals to obtain Probationers, in as much as the training is not recognised for a certificate unless a year's training is obtained in a General Hospital. General Hospitals, almost without exception, decline to afford this facility." As ever, central administration fails to take notice of the actual problems in the field, an attitude so often encountered later in the century.

In 1918 we have record of another lady doctor being on the staff, Mrs G.E. Bartlett, who was Assistant Surgeon. Queen Alexandra again made a donation to the general funds, this time of £100 from the Alexandra Day fête and the following year she allocated £100 to the Building Fund.

In 1918 the Armistice brought the war to an end on 11th November and a period of rehabilitation was required by the whole country to recover from the most severe experience that it had yet undergone. Even then, plans were being considered to enlarge the hospital further, though it was to be two years before they were completed.

Apparently the school was discontinued for a short time in 1917 but, towards the end of 1918, it was re-opened under the guidance of Mrs Catherine Howland. Numbers gradually rose until some 120 children under treatment in the hospital were receiving schooling. Under the aegis of the Royal Sea Bathing Hospital Committee, this school continued until the Second World War when the hospital was evacuated on account of the Battle of Britain.

Miss Doughty was Cub Master of the Wolf Cub Pack in the hospital, formed by Miss Phyllis East, her cousin. The pack was a most enthusiastic one and was very proud of winning the Annual Competition one year in the face of competition from physically fit packs in the Isle of Thanet. The 32nd Margate Troop of Rover Scouts was also founded at the Royal Sea Bathing Hospital for the older boys. They were taught activities which could be carried out while they were still confined to bed, such as signalling, map-reading, first aid and Morse code and were provided with buzzers for sending and receiving Morse.

Miss Doughty taught in the school for some years prior to the Second World War and subsequently became Mrs Howland's daughter-in-law when she married Mr Howland, later chairman of the League of Friends of the Royal Sea Bathing Hospital.

An old patient was Annie Eve Packer who returned her thanks "to doctors, matron and treatment"! Rev. Henry O. Grove, the Archdeacon of London, again came down to remind us of his stay in the hospital fifty years previously.

The plans for a further extension were agreed on 4th October 1919 when the Ministry of Health provided £10,880, essentially as a loan under the National Insurance Act of 1911 and the Finance Act of the same year. It was provided ". . . to be utilised primarily for the reception and treatment of discharged Sailors and Soldiers suffering from non-pulmonary tuberculosis" (C & T DHA Doc.8). The first tender for its erection was for £15,812, although greater outlays were expected. The wards are dated 1919 and were opened by HRH Princess Alice in 1920 and named "King George V Wards".

It was in 1919 also that Miss Kempson, the Matron, was awarded the RRC First Class, a great honour for the hospital.

Dr Llewellyn Rees, Portadown, and Lt. Col. E.M. Illington, of the Indian Medical Service, visited the hospital on 25th July 1919 and recalled

K.G.2 Ward.

Two-storey Nurses' Home.

that they had been Resident Surgeons in the hospital. It seems likely that Colonel Illington had married the Matron when he was here, as Miss Hilberry, who subsequently became Mrs Illington, retired in 1897 and lived until 1939. There is a memorial to her in the chapel. Mrs Rees also visited the hospital at about this time. It may be guessed, though it is no more than a guess, that Drs Rees and Illington deprived the hospital of a Sister and a Matron when they were residents here as Mrs Rees recorded that she had been a Sister at the hospital from 1892 to 1894!

Mr John Dickson, Consulting Orthopaedic Surgeon in the city of Ipswich, reminds us that his father, Dr Dickson, was one of the Resident Surgeons at the Royal Sea Bathing Hospital during 1920, so he himself continues in the tradition of orthopaedic surgery. Sir D'Arcy Power, on one of his visits to the hospital in 1921, repeated the Visiting Surgeons' recommendation of 1888 that the hospital should have its own Splint Workshop but extraordinarily, it was not until 1924 that this dream became the reality of the superb Hospital Splint-making Department that ultimately developed. Sir D'Arcy Power was a most active member of the London Medical Board and regularly came down to Margate and took the chair at many Board Meetings. His death in 1940 was a very great loss to the hospital.

Three old patients signed the Visitors' Book that year, recalling how they were under treatment here, H.C. Clarke in Lettsom Ward in 1917, Ada Longhurst in 1889 and Henry Tovey "about 45 years ago". They all expressed their appreciation of the treatment they had received and attributed their present good health to their stay at the Royal Sea Bathing Hospital. Sister Banyard recorded that she had been a Sister in Lettsom in the 1920s, and she may have known Clarke, as she does not state when she started. Rev. H.L. Hubbard was appointed as Hospital Chaplain in 1921 and held the post for almost twenty years, retiring in 1940.

An important addition to the hospital was made in 1922 and this was the provision of a two-storey Nurses' Home. The cost of this was £13,480, including the furnishings.

Miss Hardman was a probationer at this time and returned twenty-four years later as Home Sister and Second Assistant Matron.

1923 was marked by an event of the first importance when Dr Basil Armstrong, OBE, MC, was appointed Medical Superintendent on 16th April. Much will be heard of him later for he left an indelible mark, not only on the hospital but also on the national approach to the treatment of surgical tuberculosis. He was a great technician with plaster-of-Paris and a great mechanician, developing many splints and appliances and Sir D'Arcy Power's workshops in which to make them.

Dr Armstrong was the whole doctor. He knew each and every patient in the most complete and intimate way, taking most meticulous histories, making most exhaustive clinical notes and entering into every detail of their lives, from their birthdays, hobbies, likes and dislikes to the particulars of

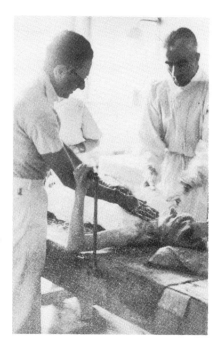

Dr Basil Armstrong (at right) plastering.

"their sisters and their cousins and their aunts"! Not only so, but when they returned to the hospital from all over the country (and in those days the Royal Sea Bathing Hospital was a National Institution and drew patients from every county) for follow-up examination or simply to visit the hospital again, which many of them did, he recognised them and remembered them in every detail.

The Resident Surgeons at the hospital in 1922 were both ladies, namely Miss Margaret McLaren and Miss Henrietta Jebens. The latter was to become one of the best known lady Orthopaedic Surgeons of the years after the Second World War.

But to return to Dr Armstrong, while he did not "write up" a great series of cases of any particular aspect of the disease, he made a number of more general contributions to surgical literature from time to time (RSBHA 291-295). He might well have written more, for he accumulated an unrivalled experience of every aspect of surgical tuberculosis in the thirty-one years of his tenure of the Medical Superintendent's post.

As indicated in a previous paragraph, he followed-up the patients for their own benefit almost indefinitely so that he might be certain that their disease was remaining quiescent or so that he might catch any recrudescence or re-emergence of the disease elsewhere at the earliest possible moment.

Dr Armstrong was personally responsible for the development of a morale amongst doctors, nurses, lay staff, patients and friends that remains to this day. In illustration of this contention, it may be remarked that the patients who returned to the hospital so regularly, often from far afield, did so entirely at their own expense. There was no National Health Service to provide free transport to hospital, and many of the patients were originally children and many of them came from the poorest strata of society. Somehow they managed to find the necessary finance to return to Margate, how they did so, one can but guess, but there was a steady flow to Dr Armstrong's "follow-up" sessions. And, to be sure, they would, on arrival, be greeted by name, with enquiries about their wedding, their children, their job or whatever will have been important to them individually.

There is no doubt that Dr Armstrong was a remarkable man.

As previously mentioned, Miss Kempson, the Matron, died on 3rd October 1923. She was followed by another Miss Kempson, Miss Joan Kempson this time. This was her sister who also came to the Royal Sea Bathing Hospital from St George's Hospital. Another appointment that year was of Mr F.R. Wallis as Dental Surgeon. He served until the later 1960s and then became a great force in the "Friends of the Royal Sea Bathing Hospital", who did, and continue to do, so much for all aspects of hospital work that fall outside the remit of the National Health Service. The Nurses' Recreation Hall was named in his memory and filled an important place in the facilities of the hospital. At the same time, Dr Babington was appointed as Ophthalmic Surgeon and C.J. Terrier as Assistant Surgeon.

The training of nurses continued to give rise to problems but Sister Stewart, the Sistor Tutor, managed at this time to obtain liaisons with Guy's Hospital and the Ipswich and East Suffolk Hospital (the latter possibly through the good offices of Dr Dickson) whereby the nurses could complete their training at these hospitals. Their two years training at the Royal Sea Bathing Hospital was allowed to count as one year towards their general training. Mrs Parsons subsequently took over the post of Sister Tutor and continued with the development of affiliations with general hospitals. She was able to conclude an agreement with the St Marylebone Hospital, so improving the nursing prospects further. Some nurses came to the Royal Sea Bathing Hospital already fully trained and one of these was a Miss Hogg who joined the staff in 1924 and later became Office Sister, a post she held for eighteen years, and subsequently Night Sister until her retirement in 1946. She is seen receiving congratulations from HRH Princess Alice in a photograph reproduced in Chapter Nine.

In 1922 radio broadcasting began when the station at Savoy Hill went "on the air" with the famous identification signal: "2LO". Not only could radio signals be received but they could be transmitted to the wards. So reception to the K.G. Wards at this time was provided through the kindness of Messrs Keeley, Cleveland and Redman. This was primarily for the benefit of ex-servicemen who were still under treatment and included some who had been gassed in the war.

It was in 1923 that Miss E.E. Smeeton returned to the hospital to tell of how she had been a Staff Nurse on Maud Ward in 1908. She must have been a contemporary of Nurse Hicks. It was also in the same year that George Judkins, J.H. Tomkins, J.F. Hutchins and Rosa Blackwood revisited the scene of their treatment.

There were not only individual visitors to the hospital but organisations of various kinds, for example, the Edmonton Board of Guardians. Mr A. Mahon, on behalf of that Board, which had some of its Wards in as patients, recorded in the Visitors' Book on 28th March 1924 that he found all the Board's patients very happy and comfortable and considered that great praise was due to the staff.

Amongst those who regularly supported the Royal Sea Bathing Hospital down the years were the City Livery Companies and the Corporation of London itself, its donations starting in 1800. The Goldsmiths contributed from 1802 and the Mercers from 1851. Both the Grocers' and the Clothworkers' Companies also made considerable contributions and altogether some twenty-two City Livery Companies figure in the subscription lists. It is of interest that many of these subscriptions ceased at the outbreak of the First World War: several stopped after 1923 and others after 1933 and 1937 was the last date of any Livery Company donations. However, as will be seen in the list of acknowledgements, several of them made handsome contributions towards the publication of this volume!

Dr, later Sir Robert, Hutchison became a member of the London Medical Board in 1925. Famous for his writings, particularly on diseases of children, he subsequently became President of the Royal College of Physicians and one of a remarkable trio, namely himself, Sir Hugh Lett and Sir Eardley Holland, Presidents of the Royal College of Surgeons and the Royal College of Obstetricians and Gynaecologists respectively, who were not only all Presidents of their respective Royal Colleges at the same time but were all on the staff of the same hospital, The London Hospital. It is believed that such a record is unique. Both Sir Robert Hutchison and Sir Hugh Lett visited the hospital in 1930 or thereabouts.

Many other famous surgeons visited the hospital, including Sir Arbuthnot Lane, Sir Max Page, Mr Jenner Verrall and Mr Lambrinudi. Lambrinudi, in fact, assisted Dr Armstrong in the performance of a hindquarter operation, the most serious and heroic operation in the field of orthopaedic surgery.

During the second Miss Kempson's period of office, one of the splintmakers, Geoff Ells, was a very accomplished sculptor. He carved a crucifix in wood for Miss Kempson but sadly did not live to complete it and one arm remained to be fashioned. Miss Kempson sent it to Oberammergau to have it finished and it now stands in the chapel.

Chapter 8
THE DOLLS

The visits of old patients continued after the war and in 1926 L. Lisney returned on 9th September and recalled how he had been a patient from 1911 to 1914, for treatment of disease of the spine. He reported that he was "going strong now"!

The very long stay indicates the very long time that the treatment of tuberculosis of the spine took in the days before antibiotic therapy. This was particularly the case in children, where the disease used to spread widely and affect many vertebrae, resulting in terrible deformities.

But nevertheless, these patients did recover under the regime of rest in bed under the best hygienic conditions on a light nutritious diet and with their bodily needs attended to, with regular hours and long periods of sleep. As will be remembered from earlier pages, the diet was often very far from light, but no doubt this applied to those who were on the road to recovery and were able to accept what appear to us today to have been "man-sized" meals!

At this time, exposure of the skin to the elements was part of the treatment and Dr Armstrong had a very carefully calculated system of progressive exposure so as to make sure that patients did not experience sun-burn. But the Vitamin D which in this way was synthesized in the skin undoubtedly played an important part in their recovery.

Dr Armstrong's Instructions for Sun-Bathing: (These should be taken in conjunction with the Diagram).

"SUN-BATHING"

"Next to sufficiently prolonged rest, outdoor treatment is perhaps the most powerful weapon we have in the fight against tuberculous infection.

"Under outdoor treatment we include the exposure of the body surface to the effects of sun and wind.

"A patient whose skin tans well, usually does well and it is important that we should try, during the summer months, to see that a considerable degree of pigmentation is attained.

"Pigmentation is, of course, Nature's barrier against an *excessive* dose of ultra-violet radiation in which sunlight is very rich.

"Ultra-violet radiation is believed to encourage the production in the deeper layers of the skin of substances which promote health and raise the resistance of the body to bacterial infection.

"An excess of ultra-violet light upon a skin, unprotected by pigmentation, will produce a painful sunburn often going on to blistering and may

1The result of tuberculosis of the spine in childhood, possibly the inspiration for "Mr Punch".

	DAYS OF TREATMENT											
	1	2	3	4	5	6	7	8	9	10	11	12
IIIa				MINUTES OF TREATMENT								
				5	10	15	20	25	30	35	40	45
IIa			5	10	15	20	25	30	35	40	45	50
Ia		5	10	15	20	25	30	35	40	45	50	55
I	5	10	15	20	25	30	35	40	45	50	55	60

Armstrong's sun-bathing chart.

116

do considerable harm to the general health in addition, and it is important therefore that sunlight should be administered cautiously and over only gradually increasing periods in order to produce the necessary pigmentation to protect against an excessive dose.

"Special care is necessary in the case of fair-haired, and particularly red-haired, persons. In these, the pigment of the skin, instead of being evenly distributed, tends to be clumped together in little islands, known as freckles. While the freckles pigment deeply in sunlight, the areas of skin between them are relatively devoid of pigmenting substance and are very liable to sunburn.

"Nevertheless, many fair-haired people do possess a sufficiency of general pigment to afford them protection if tanning is very slowly and cautiously developed.

"*Pigmentation* not only protects the body against excess of ultra-violet light, but allows it to stand without discomfort greater exposure to heat, cold and wind, all powerful factors in producing bodily well-being.

"Particular caution in the administration of sunlight is desirable in the case of seriously ill patients and those suffering from active pulmonary tuberculosis. It should be withheld from patients who are 'running' a temperature.

"In general, the best hours for sun-bathing are between 9 o'clock and midday. It may sometimes be advisable to take patients into their wards if the heat of the day becomes excessive."

Dr Armstrong's dosage started at five minutes and increased by five minutes a day, starting with the front of the legs, then with the front of the thighs and back of the legs, the front of the trunk and the back of the thighs and finally with the back of the trunk. Full protection would then be reached by about the fifteenth day. Each previously exposed part would have the new dosage added to that which it had already achieved.

Any interruption of the treatment set the patient back two days but, of course, if the interruption were prolonged, the course might have to be re-started further back. However, it was often modified by allowing the treatment pattern to be repeated two or three times in the day after a patient had got well into the programme.

Dr Armstrong's regime is illustrated in the accompanying diagram which is based on his own illustration used in conjunction with the text given above.

One wonders if the sun shone much more reliably in Margate in those days!

Nowadays the preoccupation with "skin cancer" might negative this treatment, should it still be thought helpful (although the principle could well be applied by the holiday-maker in, for example, the Mediterranean area), but it is doubtful if the sun at Margate is ever as threatening as it is in

117

Fred Christian, after his retirement.

Queensland! As it is, however, tuberculosis is so much a thing of the past, and the drug treatment so successful, that the need for this form of adjuvant therapy no longer arises.

In 1926 the House Surgeons, and this is the first time we read of this designation, were P.V. Crameri and L.D. Richards.

The following year S. Brittain of Northampton came down to Margate and wrote in the Visitors' Book: "A returned patient. Perfectly well and grateful fourteen years since discharge". It was in this year also that it was confirmed that nothing in this world is perfect and the Royal Sea Bathing Hospital had its downs as well as its ups. Two House Surgeons (and there is nothing to connect them with those mentioned in the previous paragraph) disgraced themselves by repeatedly coming in in the early hours of the morning drunk and disorderly, using offensive language and making such a noise that they not only woke nurses and patients but residents in Canterbury Road opposite. On the matter being referred to the Governors, it was also pointed out that they were not allowed both to be out of the hospital at the same time. There was some discussion as to whether they should be dismissed or allowed to resign. It was felt that the former course might place a life-long "black mark" upon them and so they were allowed to resign.

In 1929 we read of an Assistant Medical Superintendent becoming necessary and the post was filled by a Dr W.J. O'Connor. It was in this year, on 26th September, that Caroline Eliot Edlmann paid the last of the visits to the Royal Sea Bathing Hospital of Lettsom's descendants. The following year saw the appointment of a youth to the splint shops straight out of school. His name was Frederick Christian. Mr Christian remained as Splintmaker to the Royal Sea Bathing Hospital until his retirement in 1980, by which time he had completed fifty years of service to the hospital.

Christian entered fully into the spirit of the work and developed a very high standard of technical excellence, stimulated by the enthusiasm of Dr Armstrong. In consequence, every splint that was made for the patients was tailor-made to a perfect fit. This was achieved by first class craftsmanship, coupled with great pains in the actual fitting, repeated if necessary, until the desired result was achieved. Even so, it became routine to expect splints and braces of every kind to be ready for the patient within forty-eight hours, a period which may be compared with the two or three months which often ensued when, later, private contractors were employed by the Ministry of Health to provide splints, at least, in some hospitals!

At this time Dr Armstrong acquired a number of beautiful dolls with porcelain faces, eyes that closed when they were lain down, articulated limbs and real hair. These were fitted with various splints, made by Christian, plasters made by Armstrong himself and beds made by the hospital engineers, to illustrate some of the methods of treatment of bone and joint tuberculosis used in those days. The dolls' clothes and the bed linen were made by members of the nursing staff.

These dolls remain on show at the hospital to the present time and constitute some of the hospital's most treasured possessions. They provide not only a delightful commentary on the treatment of bone and joint tuberculosis in the 1930s and 1940s but also illustrate some of the principles in use today, as well as showing examples of several classical splints devised by such giants of the past as Thomas, Liston and Bradford.

The splint shops were used to make every part of a splint including the necessarily mechanically perfectly accurate knee joints for calipers. In the 1970s pressure of work made it necessary to purchase these components by bulk buying from outside manufacturers, but the modern joints so obtained are in no way superior to those which used to be made for decades in the hospital's own workshops by Christian and the team which he trained up to help in the work.

It is sad to have to recall that, when Christian completed his fifty years of service, no notice of any kind was taken of the event by the administration of the District which then had authority over the Royal Sea Bathing Hospital. This is a small example of the way in which Central Administration is liable to overlook the finer points and human relations which go so far to creating loyalty and a spirit of service which should be considered of first importance in the National Health Service. However, such individual consideration does not appear on any of the "returns" or attract the approbation of headquarters and so is not worth worrying about in administrative offices. The label "Morale" does not appear over any of their pigeon-holes.

Subsequently, happily, as a result of pressure from members of the hospital itself, suitable presentations were made but they failed to salute the occasion in the way in which it should have been celebrated. "Bis dat qui cito dat" remains as true today as it did 2,000 years ago. (He gives double who gives at once. Syrus, 1st century.)

In the year 1930 an Australian, Dr Thomas King, was House Surgeon at the Royal Sea Bathing Hospital. He subsequently returned to Australia and took up the specialty of Orthopaedics and went on to become the President of the Australian Orthopaedic Association in 1957. Amongst other contributions, he made a most important advance in the treatment of fractures of the neck of the femur (1934). He died in 1973.

In about 1934 Gracie Fields, the famous music hall singer, was in Margate and two of the patients wrote to her and said that the food at the Royal Sea Bathing Hospital was so bad that they were starving. Perhaps the standard had fallen or perhaps it was just that the food, although plentiful, was not very exciting. So Gracie paid a visit to Maud Ward to see for herself. It caused an enquiry — the two patients were sent home!

Eyewitnesses are always of the greatest value and personal reminiscences are equally of inestimable importance when writing a history. Mr Stanley Evernden wrote in 1976 (RSBHA 401) to Sister Mack, at that time Sister of Maud Ward. He told how he had been a patient in Maud Ward when it had been a children's ward, which it was from 1932-1935, the period of his stay in the hospital. This again illustrates the prolonged period of treatment that this serious disease, when it affected the spine, hip or sacro-iliac joint, took to reach quiescence in those days.

In his letter Mr Evernden stated: ". . . even the nursing staff, quite a few of them, contracted TB from the patients . . ." and he also commented ". . . a bedsore was a crime. I do not remember any patient who layed (sic) up to five years ever getting a red blotch, let alone a bedsore . . ." What a commentary on the superlative standard of nursing that was the rule at the Royal Sea Bathing Hospital. And the price that had to be paid by successive generations of staff for caring for the unfortunate victims of tuberculosis is again underlined. What a blessing that the disease is now contained, at least in western countries!

Mr Evernden's doctor was a Scot, a Dr Duncan who, as he reports, "used to speak his mind!" Mr Evernden remembers that Dr Armstrong's assistant was a Dr Jarvis and he sent a photograph (RSBHA 385) of the ward sister and four nurses of Maud Ward who had been amongst the staff of the ward when he was in but unfortunately he could not name them. The only two whose names he could remember are not in the photo, but they were Nurses Smith and Skinner. Nurse Smith, he tells us, married a patient named Roy Oxley, a very rich man and "very posh talking"!

Life on the ward verandas was never very comfortable. The following details give some indication of how it seemed to the patients.

". . . every bed had to be outside night and day . . . if it rained or snowed, a ground-sheet was put on the bottom of the bed. Many times I turned my pillow over as it became too wet from the rain. It was a cure only the tough ones could survive!"

". . . the nurses had to serve the meals outdoors even when it was snowing hard and a ward temperature of 45 degrees (F). During gales, beds used to be blown up and down the verandas."

". . . TB kidney was almost a sure fatal and . . . taking the diseased kidney out the other one eventually went the same way. Hips, knees were good at recovering, shoulders were not good at recovering. TB tummies were deadly."

". . . they had a very high reputation for their cure of TB of the bones. Patients came from every country in the world for treatment."

Time may have distorted the memory to some extent, but the author, having been personally a medical officer in a comparable hospital (St Luke's, Lowestoft) in the middle 1930s, can verify that there is very little that is exaggerated. Evernden reported that, when the sun was very hot in the summer, they were left out in the direct sun and could obtain no relief from the heat. This alone of his descriptions might be faulted to some extent. As mentioned a few pages back, Dr Armstrong was most particular that exposure should be carefully graded (RSBHA 344). For those who were deemed to be fully acclimatised to sunbathing, Evernden's remarks may apply, but it is difficult to believe that no relief was obtainable.

1933 is important in the history of the Royal Sea Bathing Hospital, for it saw the publication of J.J. Abraham's biography of Lettsom (l.c.), from which such a clear picture can be formed of the founder of the hospital with many facts about its early days. In this year, Francis Jarman was Assistant Medical Superintendent and developed an interest in the subject of tuberculosis which was to point the direction of his life's work. He became internationally famous as a radiologist in South Wales and author of many works on tuberculosis.

In 1935, various enlargements of the hospital raised the bed strength to no fewer than 320 beds and this, of course, meant more staff, so that an enlargement of the Nurses' Home became necessary and two more floors were added.

One visitor on 28th December 1935 was Miss Christina Foyle, head of the famous bookshop in Charing Cross Road and a leading literary figure of the day and, indeed, of the post-war era as well. She had herself been a patient at the hospital as a child for a time and was also to visit the hospital

It is my opinion that Lettsom's fame will ultimately depend on the fact that he founded the Sea Bathing Infirmary at Margate — the first hospital in the world for thalessotherapy

Johnston Abraham

22 Queen Anne St
W1

30 · VI · 33

Abraham's manuscript inscription on the fly-leaf of his "Life of Lettsom".

again over thirty years later to present prizes to the nurses. Her signature in the Visitors' Book is the last entry in a volume which served for so long and which provides us with so many vignettes of the history of the hospital (l.c.).

Miss Foyle writes: "All the memories I have of it (the Royal Sea Bathing Hospital) are happy. The nurses were so kind and I made many friends among the children. The only very sad thing was the big wards of injured and shell-shocked soldiers who used to scream. It left a deep impression on me and made me hate war."

A curious item in the records of the hospital refer to a certain Rev. W.H. Churchill, who resigned as "gardener" as he was now eighty years old and getting very deaf!

In 1936 Mr Nash retired as Hospital Secretary after thirty-six years of service, a longer period than any other member of the staff except Mr Christian.

In May of the same year Mr Lambrinudi of Guy's Hospital, for many years a regular supporter of the Royal Sea Bathing Hospital, again assisted Dr Armstrong at a very major orthopaedic operation, namely, the disarticulation through the joint of a tuberculous hip. The anaesthetic was administered by Dr Wallis and comprised spinocain, gas, oxygen and ether. About this time Mr Edgar Freshman settled in Canterbury and specialised in genito-urinary surgery. As tuberculosis so often affected the kidneys, he was an invaluable addition to the Visiting Staff and remained so until his retirement in 1964.

On 19th January 1936 the country was distressed by Lord Dawson of Penn's memorable bulletin: "The King's life is moving peacefully towards its close" and during the night of 20th January HM King George V died at Sandringham. He was succeeded by King Edward VIII.

After a reasonable interval, application was made to the Keeper of the Privy Purse to have the royal patronage renewed under the new monarch. The following letter was received:

"Dear Sir, I am desired to inform you that, owing to the necessity for restricting the number of institutions and associations to which the King gives his patronage, His Majesty regrets that it is not possible to extend this privilege to the Royal Sea Bathing Hospital, Margate. At the same time, the King sends his best wishes for the future welfare of the hospital. Yours truly (signed) Wigram, Keeper of the Privy Purse. The Chairman, The Royal Sea Bathing Hospital, Margate." (RSBHA 11A)

In view of the King's refusal, investigations were put in train to see whether the description "Royal" in the hospital's name could be retained or not. The following rather indecisive letter was received from the Central Bureau of Hospital Information:

"Dear Sir,   17th July 1936
    In reply to your letters of 7th and 9th July, Mr Baynes says: 'I cannot find
any restriction on the use of the word "royal" as part of the name — except
for companies formed under the Companies Acts, but I imagine that it is
usually assumed, when special permission is granted. I feel sure that the
hospital is entitled to continue to use its old title, though I can find no
definite authority on the point.'
    Yours truly, R.H. Poule, Director and Hon. Secretary, BHA.
The Secretary, The Royal Sea Bath *(sic)* Hospital, Margate, 15 York
Buildings, WC2." (The address of the London Secretary of the hospital.)

    On 16th July 1936 the Hospital Secretary received a letter from the Earl
of Athlone, President of the Hospital, as follows:

"Kensington Palace, W8.   16th July 1936
    . . . Lord Athlone asked me to acknowledge the receipt of your letter and
to say that he regrets you did not send in your application through him as
then he might have been able to do something for you.
    However, his Lordship would like to know exactly what is meant by the
statement in your report of 1901 as to the hospital being continuously
honoured by royal patronage, does this mean that since King George III
every reigning monarch has been patron of your hospital?
    Yours faithfully,
(Signed) Janet A.E. Harkness, Private Secretary)."

    On 18th November, Mr Gerard Wallop, Chairman of the Court of
Directors, wrote to the President of the hospital, the Earl of Athlone,
saying that he trusted that (His Majesty) would graciously reconsider his
decision.
    On 19th November 1936 the Earl of Athlone wrote to Mr Wallop from
the Guards' Club, Brook Street, W1.

"Dear Wallop,
    Yes, I agree. When I heard from the Secretary what had happened, I
asked whether the hospital case had been properly stated and I found that it
had not. I thought it best to wait for a time and I will now have a try. I wish
the secretary had written to me about the application as other Hosps etc,
with which I am connected did.
    Yours sincerely, Athlone." (RSBH 11A)

    It had been established that the royal patronage, which had been
instituted by The Prince of Wales in 1791, had subsequently been continued
by every ruling monarch.
    On 16th December 1936 King Edward VIII abdicated.
    On the same day, the Hospital Secretary, Mr Mayo, wrote to the Earl of
Athlone asking if his help could now be enlisted to apply for the royal

124

Eileen Ashcroft talking to girl patients.

patronage to the new monarch, King George VI "when you consider the time opportune".

As a result of the Earl's support, the following letter was received:

"1st February 1937   Privy Purse Office,
                                                    Buckingham Palace, SW.
Dear Sir,

I am commanded by the King to inform you that His Majesty has been graciously pleased to grant his patronage to the Royal Sea Bathing Hospital, Margate.

Yours truly, Ulick Alexander, Keeper of the Privy Purse.
The Chairman, The Royal Sea Bathing Hospital, Margate." (RSBH 11A)

On 12th February 1937 the Earl of Athlone wrote to the Hon. Gerard Wallop, JP: "It gives me great satisfaction to hear from Major Alexander that the King has granted his patronage to the hospital and I am delighted to have been able to arrange this." (RSBH 11A)

So the royal patronage was interrupted by King Edward VIII's refusal but happily reinstated by King George VI and we see another example of the practical way in which the Earl of Athlone exercised his office of President.

However, the Earl of Athlone had to interrupt his connection with the hospital for a time, as this minute of the Report of the Court of Directors for 1939 indicates:

"HM the King has been graciously pleased to approve of the appointment of Major-General the Earl of Athlone, KG, as Governor-General of the Dominion of Canada.

"Your Directors desire to preface their Annual Report with this important official announcement, and to extend to our President, Lord Athlone, their warm congratulations and sincere good wishes for His Lordship's success in the great Imperial Office to which he has been appointed. Their good wishes are also extended to Princess Alice who, it is assured, will make an inestimable contribution to his success by her instant popularity."

It is remarkable that, at this time, the recruitment of nurses has eased considerably and now affiliations had been established with the Radcliffe Hospital at Oxford and the Hertford County Hospital for continuation of the nurses' general training.

In the "Daily Mirror" of 9th February 1939 Eileen Ashcroft reported that she had visited the hospital and named some of the children she had seen, including Patricia Ingrin Johnson, Maureen Dolan, aged two years and two months, Mary Rowe and Edna M. George. She remarked that the Royal Sea Bathing Hospital was ". . . one of the most cheerful hospitals in England . . . the surroundings of the hospital are ideal and in no hospital have I ever seen the patients look happier." (Reports 1936-41, p.712)

126

Chapter 9

THE SECOND WORLD WAR AND
THE 150TH ANNIVERSARY

But the war clouds were gathering over Europe and the Western Powers, including Great Britain, were re-arming frantically. This meant rocketing taxes so that no individual was any longer left with any money over and above his daily needs to spare for charity. This sounded the death knell for the voluntary hospital system as all such hospitals went rapidly into debt, were taken over by the Emergency Medical Service during the war and fell, like ripe plums, into the hands of the government after the war.

In March 1939 the hospital had been scheduled to participate in the Emergency Medical Service and supplementary beds and equipment were supplied by the Ministry of Health so that, by the outbreak of war at the beginning of September, the normal peacetime complement of 320 beds had been increased to 520. It is remarkable that the hospital lent itself to the possibility of such a great increase in its bed strength and this was, in part, in anticipation of the huge number of air raid casualties which never developed in East Kent or elsewhere, at least until the following year.

In accordance with Ministry instructions, all patients who were well enough were sent to their homes and during the first three days of September the occupied beds were reduced from 314 to 170. Certain wards were entirely cleared of ordinary patients and were prepared for the reception of "casualties".

After a quiet start, as far as Britain was concerned, the war flared up in May 1940, when the Germans occupied the whole of the coastline of the continent facing Britain. This led to the historic evacuation of Dunkirk and the landing of tens of thousands of troops in East Kent. Many of these were wounded and the Royal Sea Bathing Hospital acted as a Casualty Clearing Station during May and June and some 400 wounded military personnel received their primary treatment here.

So full was the hospital at this time that the chapel had to be used as extra ward accommodation. Many soldiers were even unconscious when admitted. One of these, on recovering consciousness and seeing all the stained glass around him with its religious themes, said to his neighbour: "Open your eyes, Mate, we're in Heaven at last." This sentiment was curiously almost exactly duplicated many years later one Christmas in the wards. (Chapter 14).

South Hill Park, Bracknell.

The air battle now started to rage directly over the hospital, which was now right in the front line of the Battle of Britain. With the air saturated with military aircraft, Margate no longer remained the healthiest place in England and therefore the hospital was compulsorily closed and evacuated to South Hill Park, Bracknell, near Bagshot, the children being transferred in May and the adults in June. During this time, Miss Hilda Harcourt was promoted from Theatre Sister, a post she had held since 1935, to be Matron. She made a highly efficient matron and so continued until her retirement in 1964. While the hospital was at Bracknell, Dr A.E. Russell, MD, FRCP, a former member of the Medical Board, acted as Official Visitor as he lived nearby (Reports, 1940, p.11).

As soon as the war ended, patients were brought back to the Royal Sea Bathing Hospital and it was re-opened on 12th October 1945. During the last year at Bracknell, Dr J.A. MacKenzie assumed the appointment of Assistant Medical Superintendent and remained as Dr Armstrong's able assistant for five or six years.

One of the most significant episodes during the war was the bombing of the Headquarter Offices of the Royal Sea Bathing Hospital in London. In consequence, a great many most precious records were lost and it is fortunate that so many were housed at Margate. But even then, as has been noted, the storage was so indifferent that many of them were so damaged by water as to be useless.

The 150th Anniversary of the Founding of the Royal Sea Bathing Hospital fell in 1941 when Britain was at war and standing alone against Germany. The country was at full stretch and, indeed, that year was the lowest point of the war. It was obviously impossible to consider any

128

150th Anniversary of the first admission of patients in 1796. 23rd July 1946. HRH Princess Alice, Countess of Athlone and the Earl of Athlone (formerly Alexander of Teck), President of the Royal Sea Bathing Hospital. The group is: Miss Harcourt, Matron, Dr Basil Armstrong, Medical Superintendent, the Earl of Athlone, Major General Lord Annaly, Chairman of the Court of Directors, F.J. Cornford, Esq., JP, Major of Margate, Princess Alice, Miss J. Basset, Mayoress of Margate and Miss Olive Monahan, Assistant Matron.

celebrations and the hospital itself had been evacuated to Bracknell, so that that particular anniversary had to pass unnoticed, or at least, unsung!

However, after the war was over and the hospital had returned to its Margate home, it became apparent that a celebration of an almost parallel anniversary would be feasible, the 150th anniversary of the first opening of the hospital to receive patients in 1796.

The 23rd July 1946 was accordingly selected and a considerable programme arranged. Her Royal Highness, Princess Alice, Countess of Athlone consented to attend the occasion, accompanied by her husband, Major-General the Earl of Athlone and by Lord Annaly, Chairman of the Court of Directors of the hospital.

The Chairman and Directors assembled at Victoria Station in London at 9.45 a.m. to receive Her Royal Highness and the Earl of Athlone. The special train left Victoria at 10.10 a.m. and arrived at Margate at 12.10 p.m.

A note on the arrival of the train at Margate reads: ". . . conveyances from the station . . . something better than the local cabs. (!) Advise number of persons and conveyances required . . ." Mrs Francis recalls how an apparently ancient Rolls-Royce was called into service to meet the Earl and Countess.

129

Princess Alice meeting Sister Hogg.

Princess Alice, Miss Harcourt and Sister Tasker of New Ward, talking to a boy patient.

A real touch of Alice in Wonderland coloured the occasion because one of the splint-makers, a very tall man, was deputed to tie artificial blooms onto some small trees that lined the driveway of the hospital. This, it was hoped, would brighten the Princess's approach. History does not tell if he got away with his head! Even though the "Queen of Hearts" could scarcely be bettered as a description of Princess Alice, I am sure she did not take her cue from Lewis Carroll's Queen!

The Annual Court of Governors met at the hospital at 12.30 p.m. under the Chairmanship of the President, the Earl of Athlone, KG. During this time, HRH Princess Alice was entertained by the Matron. Doreen Tipping, aged eight, a patient who had recently undergone an operation, presented a bouquet to Her Royal Highness. Luncheon was taken at 1.15 p.m.

The menu for the 150th Anniversary Celebratory Luncheon on 23rd July 1946 was a simple one, as may be seen below, and the meal was planned to take an hour and a half. No doubt the speeches were brief and allowed the subsequent activities to proceed according to the timetable. In his speech, Sir Edgar Waterlow, proposing the toast of Lettsom, suggested that a bronze plaque should be put up in the chapel in his memory (Isle of Thanet Gazette, 1946). The brass plate which was put up in consequence has already been mentioned in the description of the chapel.

MENU
Consomme Madrilleine
Salmon Mayonnaise
Poulet Chaud Froid *(sic)*
Salade à la Russe
Salade Francaise
Glace à la Vanille
ou
Glace Fraise
Café

The toast list was as follows:

HM The King, our Patron	The President
HM The Queen, HM Queen Mary,	
Members of the Royal Family	The President
Major-General the Rt. Hon. the Earl of Athlone,	
our President and HRH Princess Alice,	The Rt. Hon.
Countess of Athlone	Lord Annaly, MC
Dr John Coakley Lettsom, our Founder	Sir Edgar Waterlow, Bart., MA

(I suppose you cannot drink the health of someone who is dead. Presumably glasses were raised to his memory!)

Princess Alice talking to Richard Pyle, a boy patient.

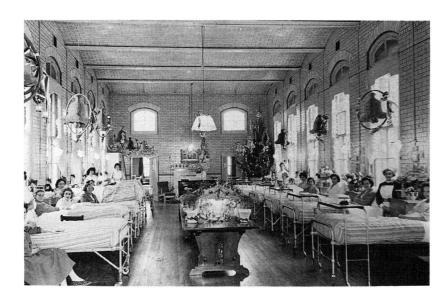

Alexandra Ward with Sister D'Arcy (at right).

Our Guests, coupled with the names of the Mayor and
Mayoress of Margate (Ald. F.J. Cornford, JP, CC
and Miss J. Bassett)   Mr A. Van den Bergh

After lunch, there was a tour of the hospital, starting at 2.45 p.m., while
an orchestra played on the lawn. This was followed by photographs and tea.
During the afternoon, Sisters Hogg and Hardman were given presentations
and introduced to Princess Alice in recognition of their long years of service
to the hospital.

A Service of Thanksgiving was also held before the end of the celebration.
Invitations to the ceremony were divided into those invited for lunch at
1 p.m. and tea, and those invited for tea only at 2.30 p.m. Those accepting
invitations for lunch were: The Earl of Athlone and HRH Princess Alice,
The Mayor and Mayoress of Margate, Lord Annaly, Mr and Mrs A. Van
den Bergh, B. Guy Harrison, Esq., I. Hope Gosse, Esq., Mr and Mrs R.A.
Hickling, R.A. Young, Esq., Dr and Mrs Parrott, Mr and Mrs W.E.C.
Wynne, Major and Mrs Babington, F.R. Wallis and Miss Wallis, Sir Henry
Markham, Dr and Mrs Brockhurst, The Editor, the Isle of Thanet Gazette,
Mrs Venner, Sub. Lt. and Mrs Treves, Mr and Mrs C.C. Maughan, Dr Basil
Armstrong, A representative of The Lancet, Sir Edgar and Lady Waterlow,
Captain and Mrs Hatfeild, Mr and Mrs H.E. Batten, Sir A.M.H. and Lady
Gray, Mr and Mrs Geoffrey Marshall, Sir Max Page, Dr and Mrs Bradley,
Dr and Mrs A.S. Wallis, C.E.S. Oxley, Esq., Rev. J.V. Markham and Miss
Markham, Miss Hilda Harcourt, Matron, Mrs Sutcliffe, The Rt. Hon.
Lady Carson, Mrs Hubbard, The Rt. Hon. the Bishop of Dover.

Carriages left at 5.10 p.m. and the train back to London left Margate
Station at 5.28 p.m.

One curious feature had become apparent on the return of the hospital
from Bracknell. During the time when it was uninhabited, its extensive
lawns had been adopted by a colony of wild rabbits. They became very tame
and used to take food from the patients, even getting, obviously with a
certain amount of help, onto the patients' beds! It was a not very welcome
invasion because they were not particularly clean. Luckily, the rabbits only
lasted a single summer.

As we approach modern times, it is possible to give more details of events
and personalities, but selectivity has still to be exercised and not everyone or
every episode can be mentioned.

Miss Olive Monahan became the Assistant Matron of the Royal Sea
Bathing Hospital in 1946 and very quickly developed an interest in the
history of the hospital. As mentioned above, her collection of records,
archives and memorabilia set the scene for the production of a major
history. In addition, she was always very much in demand to give talks and
demonstrations of photographs and other artefacts of historical interest.
She also supplemented in no little degree Dr Armstrong's effervescing

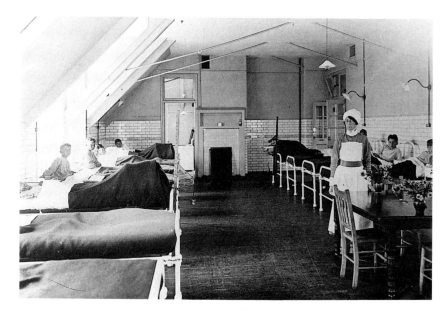

New Ward.

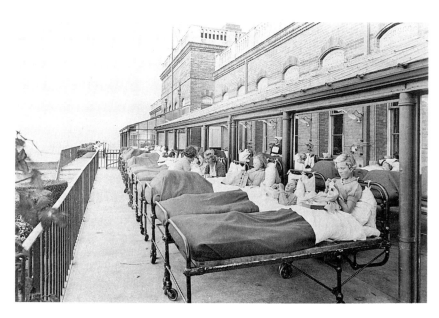

Louise Ward Balcony.

enthusiasm and thereby strengthened very greatly the remarkable morale that is the outstanding characteristic of the hospital.

Miss Hogg was in her last year as Night Sister in 1946 and Sister D'Arcy was Sister in Charge of Alexandra Ward. She was a most progressive sister and, in spite of holding the post for very many years, was always interested in new and improved methods of nursing in whatever direction they lay. Sister Peall came on the staff as a staff nurse this year and ultimately progressed to being Night Sister until she retired in March 1980. The illustrations show New Ward and the balcony of Louise Ward.

Another stride forward in medical progress had been made during the war and that was the discovery of penicillin. Until the end of the war, this powerful antibiotic had been reserved for the treatment of patients in the armed forces but, with the coming of peace, it was released for use for the general population.

It made, of course, a tremendous contribution to the treatment of tuberculosis in those cases where sinuses had become secondarily infected with pyogenic organisms. Such secondary infection was one of the major causes of mortality and morbidity, often, in former days, leading to the development of amyloid disease. This was a sort of starchy infiltration of the tissues and was usually fatal. Secondary infection used often to result in severe destruction of joints affected by tuberculosis, as, for example, in the foot, where the complicated arrangement of joints meant that the whole foot became involved and had to be amputated.

Among other advantages, penicillin rendered operations on tuberculous joints less liable to be followed by secondary infection and this made for more opportunities for surgical treatment and fewer worries about the outcome of such operations.

1947 was outstanding in the history of the treatment of tuberculosis because it was in that year that iso-nicotinic-acid-hydrazide, which came to be known as INAH, was discovered. This was one of the trio of powerful anti-tuberculous drugs which helped to revolutionise the treatment of tuberculosis in the late 1940s and early 1950s. The other anti-tuberculous drugs, para-amino-salicylic acid (PAS) and streptomycin, followed in the next four or five years.

It was also in 1947 that Mrs Cobb, widow of the great-great-grandson of Mr Cobb, the surgeon to the hospital in the 1820s, presented the letter written to Mr Cobb in 1823 by Mrs Icken, which has been recorded fully in chapter 3. The feature of particular interest in the light of today's problems which it reveals is that, even in 1823, the Royal Sea Bathing Hospital had a waiting-list!

Chapter 10

SURGICAL TUBERCULOSIS

Perhaps an outline of the treatment of bone and joint tuberculosis in the 1920s and 1930s before it was so completely revolutionised by the antibiotics may be appropriate here. Some of the hospitals in England that were concerned with this aspect of medicine at that time were the Royal Sea Bathing Hospital, St Luke's Hospital, Lowestoft, Queen Mary's Hospital for Children at Carshalton, Lord Mayor Treolar's Hospital at Alton, the Wingfield Hospital at Oxford and the Robert Jones and Agnes Hunt Hospital at Oswestry. They were associated with the names of some of the giants of orthopaedics at the time, such as Armstrong, Colvin, Pugh, Henry Gauvain, Gaythorne Girdlestone, Herbert Seddon, Robert Jones and Harry Platt.

The underlying philosophy has been outlined above, but included essentially splinting a diseased part and building up the patient's general health to combat the infection. Splintage of one variety or another often had to be maintained for months or even years and was, for some joints, supplemented by traction. Sometimes it took the form of plaster immobilisation. However, it was the normal course of the disease that joints were destroyed and it was impossible to prevent them becoming permanently stiff after they became quiescent. Therefore the splintage had to be designed to ensure that the best position for function with a stiff joint was achieved. Large "cold" abscesses were liable to develop, particularly in relation to infection affecting the spine, and this meant aspirating the pus through large, wide-bore needles under local anaesthetic and with the most careful asepsis possible. It can be imagined how severe a tax on the constitution resulted when those abscesses sometimes contained a litre of pus and refilled weekly or even more often during the active phase of the disease. Occasionally an abscess had to be opened and drained as the contents were too thick to draw through a needle but, on the whole, operation was avoided if at all possible so as to reduce the risk of secondary infection.

Spinal involvement, particularly in the dorsal region, was usually accompanied, especially in children, by very widespread bony destruction and deformity and, where abscesses developed, might be complicated by paralysis due to involvement of the spinal cord. In such cases, the operations of costo-transversectomy and antero-lateral decompression might become necessary and were aimed at relieving the pressure on the spinal cord. These were sometimes successful, though unhappily not invariably so.

Another approach to treating the abscesses was by injecting Calot's fluid into them in the hope of softening their contents to allow their more complete evacuation. When sinuses threatened or developed, aseptic dressings were undertaken but prevention of secondary infection of an open sinus was only very rarely successful.

The surgery of tuberculous lesions was very restricted in view of the possibility of causing miliary or meningeal spread, both of which usually led to a fatal outcome. Non-operative treatment was only expected to produce a fibrous union of an infected joint and this was considered vulnerable and liable to relapse if subjected to undue strains. It was actually found later that such joints might go on to bony ankylosis after many years but this knowledge really came too late to affect pre-antibiotic treatment.

In consequence, bony ankylosis was encouraged by operative arthrodesis and this was performed, where possible, by extra-articular methods, that is to say, without going into the infected joint. Great progress was made in the field of bone-grafting for this purpose and amongst the pioneers in the treatment of spine and hip disease were Fred Albee of the United States (1911, 1929) and H.A. Brittain of Norwich (1941). Others who developed similar techniques were Hibbs (1926) and Wilson (1927), both of the United States.

While such operations were possible in the spine, hip, shoulder, elbow and ankle, the knee, a commonly involved joint, did not lend itself to extra-articular fusion. Formal arthrodesis of the knee, therefore, had to be undertaken by intra-articular techniques and the risks accepted. At least one of the surgeons mentioned above used to suffuse the raw surfaces of the femur and tibia, as well as the soft tissues exposed, with anaesthetic ether before closing the wound. This was based on the rationale that ether destroyed the cell wall of the tubercle bacillus and that therefore, this treatment would prevent any organism liberated by the operation from surviving to enter the blood stream and cause remote lesions. No local ill effects were observed from this manoeuvre and it seemed to achieve the desired result.

Tuberculosis of the tarsus was often very resistant to treatment on account of the complicated arrangement of the joints of the foot, so that below-knee amputation sometimes became necessary.

A start on local chemotherapy was being made in the immediate pre-Second World War years with the use of "Prontosil" and of systemic "Uleron". The sulphonamides were in their infancy but were already holding out some prospects of benefit. However, these were really all directed against pyogenic organisms and not the tubercle bacillus itself. Again, some advantage was hoped for in the treatment of sinuses with ultra-violet light and applicators, capable of delivering the light actually within the sinuses, were being developed.

On the whole, however, drug treatment was of little value at this time. The magic name of Gold was naturally tried and weekly intra-muscular

137

Patient doing exercises on plaster bed and turning frame.

injections of Solganol-B-Oleosum were given in prolonged series without any perceptible advantage arising beyond the patient's satisfaction that he was being treated with what he imagined must surely be the most expensive drug on earth!

A wide variety of splints and plasters was devised for the proper immobilisation of the involved joints and patients were often discharged from hospital as having achieved quiescence of the disease but having to wear calipers, blocked leather splints or spinal braces of aluminium, spring steel and webbing. These ambulatory splints often had to be worn for a year or even two after completion of hospital treatment.

So much for the outline of the local treatment of bones and joints. The general treatment remained the same for a hundred and fifty years: the best that could be provided in the shape of rest, good food, good nursing and a healthy climate. Sea bathing itself had been abandoned as we have seen, but there can be no doubt that it was in many ways beneficial for not only did it clean any wounds, ulcers or sinuses but it must have been a general stimulus to the circulation which will have had a distinct influence on a patient's general condition.

In the same way, the effect of day-long exposure to the elements is no longer considered necessary but in the pre-antibiotic days had a remarkable effect on a patient's morale and feeling of well-being. At least, Lettsom's concept of "Solaria" was not misplaced and continued as a major adjuvant to the treatment regime. Even Erasmus Wilson's query about patients being in a draft was usually answered by them living out, day and night, in fair weather or in foul, on the verandas which were only covered from above but were open to the four winds of heaven otherwise. Even if a layer of snow

138

did form between each blanket when the bed was being made, no ward sister would have changed the routine for a moment!

The risk of renal infection, either during treatment or some years later, was ever present and aggravated, in cases of hip, spine or sacro-iliac disease, by the need for very long periods of recumbency, anything from one to three years and sometimes more, especially in children.

In such cases, haematuria and renal colic indicated the formation of stones in the kidney and the probability that consequent tuberculous infection of the kidney would follow. Ball and Evans (1932) stated that this was recognised but did not give any authority, whereas Key (1936), who was working at Princess Mary's Hospital at Margate, then also devoted to the treatment of children with tuberculosis, confirmed that opinion and quoted Pugh, of Queen Mary's Hospital, Carshalton (in an undated Annual Report of the London County Council), who "has long recognized the desirability of facilitating normal drainage of the renal pelvis" and refers to his frame which was rotated for a quarter of an hour "every few hours". At Lowestoft we found that the simple method of turning a patient onto his face for three hours once in three months was sufficient to prevent the formation of renal calculi.

In more modern times, patients were kept more or even permanently on their face which was better in every way and much more comfortable for them. In this way, infected areas of the spine were relieved of the pressure across the lesion that every flexion movement of the spine produced and an apparent traction, which is a normal part of the treatment of tuberculous joints, substituted with every extension movement. Not only could their kidneys drain but they could flex their knees up, they could see around the ward, reach their lockers more easily, read and write, and particularly drink, much more comfortably. Their feet hung over the lower end of the plaster, which was raised above the bed on a frame, and so avoided drop foot. Of course their beds were placed head into the ward.

In a very short time they could hold their heads up all day long. This also meant that they were no longer at risk of developing pressure sores on their backs or heels and it also showed that the strict immobilisation regime previously considered essential was no longer necessary.

Small children had been treated in the prone position for many years but it was not previously realised that adults could not only tolerate this position but be far more comfortable in it and it certainly reduced the work of the nursing staff.

Despite the severity of the disease, a high proportion of the patients recovered even though it took so long to do so. Patients with tuberculous peritonitis or salpingitis made slow progress and were liable to become sterile or to have a faecal fistula develop, an unpleasant and resistant complication. Tuberculous glands of the neck, the original "scrofula" usually healed, although sometimes surgical excision or drainage was necessary.

139

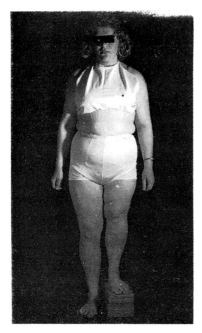

Patient with short leg due to spontaneous arrest of growth at the epiphyses during treatment for hip trouble as a child.

Two small children on their anterior plasters.

140

But tuberculosis remains a general, a crippling and a killing disease. Fatalities were due to tuberculous meningitis, miliary spread, renal infection or amyloid disease and, up to the time of the antibiotics, resulted in a perceptible proportion of cases, so giving tuberculosis its deservedly bad name.

Another very special activity in the treatment of tuberculosis of the spine and sacro-iliac joints was perfected at the Royal Sea Bathing Hospital under Dr Armstrong's guidance. This was the manufacture of superb, plaster-of-paris beds or "boats". These were made for each patient individually from multiple sheets of butter muslin dipped in plaster cream, that is, plaster powder to which the appropriate amount of water had been added immediately before, and made into a thin paste. Each layer was smoothed onto the oiled skin of the patient or on the previous layers in such a way that no air bubbles were allowed to persist between the layers and all the wrinkles were smoothed out. When approximately eighteen layers had been applied, the plaster was removed from the patient, trimmed and then dried in special drying ovens in the plaster room. When it was dry and strong, usually a week later, the patient was laid in it and a complementary shell was made for the front of the patient and treated in the same way, the two now fitting the patient and each other perfectly.

After both plasters were dry and trimmed, they were treated with seven further layers of muslin, this time each being painted into position with liquid celluloid and each layer being allowed to dry before the next was applied. In this way, the plasters were rendered completely waterproof and were so strong that they would last the patient the full time of his treatment, even if this took three years. When the patient was to be turned, the anterior shell was placed over him and strapped to the posterior one. He could now be turned onto his face and the posterior part of the plaster removed. This could therefore be achieved without in any way disturbing the position of his spine.

This turning, although an efficient technique was devised for it, remained a considerable feat for the nursing staff, particularly in a heavy patient with two plaster shells in position. In order to overcome this problem, a turning frame was devised and manufactured in the hospital splint shops, its details being streamlined by Mr Christian. This carried the two shells each in two half wheels in such a way that there was a gap between them so as not to pinch the patient's skin and also so that the half wheels bore the weight of the second shell and not the patient (Strange, 1960).

All the nurses had to do was to carry the other half shell with its half wheels attached, over the patient and place it in position, a far lighter weight than patient and two plasters, and spin him (gently, of course!) in the frame cradle in which the wheels turned and then remove the first half of the plaster. The whole arrangement was so close and comfortable a fit that it was even unnecessary to strap the plasters together for turning, the patient could not fall out, and the complete manoeuvre took literally seconds only.

However, this refinement did not come into operation until the late 1950s when the prolonged recumbency treatment of tuberculous spines was going out. But the method was used for many years for splinting after surgery for spinal fusion for non-tuberculous conditions. Many orthopaedic hospitals in the country obtained copies of the turning frame for their own use, so the Royal Sea Bathing Hospital's influence was still felt in other parts of the country.

In illustration of the problems in pre-antibiotic days, a synopsis of deaths and discharges for 1936 is characteristic. (Figures are rounded and include children and adults.) (RSBH 11A)

TB	No.	Died	Average days in hospital
Spine	3		700
with abscess	25	2	800
with sinus	5	2	580
with paraplegia	3	2	110
Sacro-iliac Jt.	10	1	780
Hip	14	2	700
with abscess	4		700
with sinus	9	2	450
Knee	12	1	400
Shoulder and elbow	1		270
with abscess	2		475
with sinus	3	2	510
Carpus, tarsus, etc.	7		360
with abscess	1		250
with sinus	3		620
Abdominal	53	1	290
Glands	26		280
with sinus	15		240

What is particularly apparent in these figures is the great difference in time needed for treatment between soft tissue and bony lesions and the very serious implication that the presence of sinuses had on the prognosis for survival. Four out of fourteen patients with spinal or hip disease with sinuses succumbed.

Again, the apparently short time in hospital for patients with paraplegia or hip disease with sinuses is due to early death causing a great reduction in the average length of stay of these patients.

142

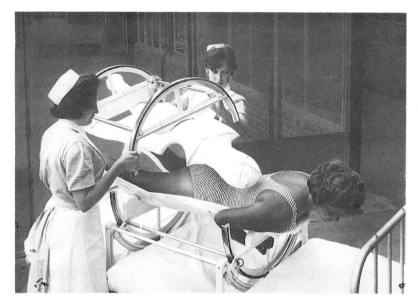

Nurses placing anterior plaster in position in preparation for turning patient in frame.

On the other hand, patients with sinuses in disease of the carpus or tarsus took a very long time to achieve recovery but they did not die. This is largely because the abscesses were much smaller and the discharge far less profuse, with consequently much less ill effect on the constitution as a whole. Locally, however, owing to the complicated nature of the joints of the wrist and foot, the disease was much more difficult to overcome in these situations.

In contrast to these results, the outcome in patients treated with the antibiotics, which have been mentioned earlier, is totally different. Sinuses are a rarity and a fatal outcome is now quite exceptional; treatment time is in days rather than years and many patients can be treated without being admitted to hospital at all.

Arising out of the greater degree of freedom that these modern methods allowed in the treatment of tuberculous joints while under anti-tuberculous drug therapy, it was found that joints could be successfully treated and still retain a high degree of mobility with safety. In the decade after the introduction of these antibiotics, in sixty-four patients with hip or knee involvement, treated at the Royal Sea Bathing Hospital, thirty-four retained at least a right-angle of movement at the end of treatment (Wright and Strange, 1965). What a contrast to the pre-antibiotic target of a firm bony or fibrous ankylosis of a joint in the best position for function! And happily, tuberculosis has become a disease of great rarity in Britain today.

143

Chapter 11
ADVENT OF
THE NATIONAL HEALTH SERVICE

The year 1948 marks the turning point in the history of medical services of every description in Britain. Punitive taxation immediately before the war and continued almost indefinitely after it rendered it impossible for charitably disposed people, however wealthy, to continue to support the Voluntary Hospitals.

Towards the end of the war, the Beveridge Report on Social Services was published and, in consequence of the Government accepting its recommendations in principle, a National Health Service was planned. It was a remarkable feat on the part of the Civil Service that so great an upheaval was smoothly achieved in the short time before 4th July 1948.

On this date, then, the Voluntary Hospitals, including the Royal Sea Bathing Hospital, ceased to exist as such and came under the aegis of the National Health Service. There were some exceptions, mostly when philosophical factors were taken into account. These included the Royal Masonic Hospital, St Vincent's Hospital, Pinner, a Roman Catholic orthopaedic hospital, the Italian Hospital, Manor House Hospital at Golders Green, the Trades Union Hospital and certain others.

Apart from providing medical treatment for every member of the community that needed it "free at the time", one of the main effects of the National Health Service (NHS) in its early days was the raising of the standard of medical staffing of provincial hospitals to heights previously undreamed of. Within five years or so, every town of any size in the country had medical staffs of teaching hospital standard and this brought two sequels in its train. The first, which was the tremendous benefit to the patients, was one that the originators of the Service had looked for and hoped for.

The second was one that seems to have been entirely unforeseen. This was a dual one of the enormous cost of maintaining the untold millions of pounds' worth of hospital premises and equipment that the Health Service had appropriated and also the tremendous pressure on the Ministry from these new and superior medical staffs to up-date the outmoded hospitals in Britain and to build, re-build and equip them to the levels demanded by sophisticated mid-century medicine.

The extremely slow start to this daunting project and the equally slow progress once a start had been made, was one of the most frustrating aspects of what should have been a very promising exercise. Initially there was little change at the Royal Sea Bathing Hospital, which continued to be run by Dr Armstrong, the Medical Superintendent, and the Matron, Miss Harcourt, assisted by Dr MacKenzie, the Assistant Medical Superintendent, and by Miss Monahan, the Assistant Matron.

Amongst the many things that set the Royal Sea Bathing Hospital above any of its sisters was the extremely high quality and generous provision of the dietary for the patients. This was, at the time, supervised by Miss Monahan. One of the effects of the new central administration was take this function away from the nursing staff and appoint a catering officer for all Thanet hospitals.

It seems that the special requirements of patients suffering from tuberculosis failed to be distinguished from those of other patients and the dietary at the Royal Sea Bathing Hospital no longer reached the previous standard. While the catering officer cannot be blamed, this appears to be an inevitable result of centralisation.

With the advent of the NHS all consultants on the staff of hospitals in the Thanet Group became technically on the staff of the Royal Sea Bathing Hospital. In practice, however, Dr Armstrong and Dr MacKenzie were left to continue their work as formerly, at least at first. Edgar Freshman, Esq., FRCS, the Urologist, continued to work in the hospital to help in the treatment of genito-urinary tuberculous infections which were all too common accompaniments or sequels of tuberculosis elsewhere.

But to revert, for the moment, to the treatment of tuberculosis, things were rapidly changing. Although there had been an epidemic of tuberculosis towards the end of the war, standards of living and nutrition had improved enormously and tuberculin testing and pasteurization had virtually eliminated bovine tuberculous infection. Mass radiography had brought thousands of cases earlier under treatment, follow-up of contacts and their isolation and treatment was carried out on a nation-wide scale and BCG inoculation was being extended. Altogether a very effective war against tuberculosis was being mounted.

Added to this was the development of the powerful anti-tuberculous drugs which have already been discussed. In consequence, pressure on the beds at the Royal Sea Bathing Hospital became markedly reduced in the early 1950s. Before this, however, change had already started. In 1949, Mr F.G. St Clair Strange, FRCS, the Orthopaedic Surgeon to Canterbury and Ramsgate, and now technically on the staff of the Royal Sea Bathing Hospital, paid a visit to the hospital. At that time, passing the hospital never seemed to reveal the slightest sign of activity there (see frontispiece), but the future held something different.

Dr Armstrong took Mr Strange round the hospital where he found 250 patients suffering from surgical tuberculosis being nursed in remarkable

The school.

proximity, there only being just enough room for a locker between the beds. The average stay of the patients was three years. It was not to be very long before it became, for patients with tuberculosis, nearer three months or even less and for many, treatment at home was to be sufficient.

The reason for the overcrowding was essentially that several wards were closed on account of shortage of nurses but there may have been other reasons too. One of the empty wards was Lettsom (!) and another, Maud. This hospital seemed to Mr Strange to be the ideal place in which to develop a long-stay orthopaedic unit as there was no such place in East Kent. In addition, the very few beds intended for orthopaedic surgery in the general hospitals were always occupied by patients who had been admitted as traumatic emergencies, so that no ordinary orthopaedic surgery could be undertaken in the area.

Bone and joint tuberculosis came within the purview of orthopaedic surgery and therefore there was no reason why, with wards being empty, the hospital should not accommodate patients suffering from orthopaedic conditions, whether tuberculous or not.

Mr Strange therefore suggested to the South East Metropolitan Regional Hospital Board that an Orthopaedic Unit be developed at the Royal Sea Bathing Hospital. The Board, advised by Dr Glyn Hughes, the Senior Administrative Medical Officer, and Dr James Fairley, his Deputy, reacted

146

favourably to the suggestion and immediately took up the refurbishing of Maud Ward for this purpose with an enthusiasm unusual in an administrative organisation.

At this time P.R. Wright, Esq., FRCS, the Orthopaedic Surgeon, was appointed to the staff of the Thanet Hospitals, with special reference to the Royal Sea Bathing Hospital. Dr Armstrong was about to retire and as well as needing an orthopaedic surgeon whose duties were to be in Thanet, it was considered that the new surgeon would have to undertake certain administrative duties and so Mr Wright's experience in the RAMC during the war, when he was DADMS in India with the rank of Lt. Colonel, would make him especially suitable for the post. He came from Oxford where he had been trained by Professors Trueta and Seddon and so had had particular experience in both "pure" orthopaedics, the treatment of tuberculosis and the handling of the victims of trauma.

So it was that, on 16th October 1952, a "cold" Orthopaedic Unit was opened at the Royal Sea Bathing Hospital consisting of sixteen beds for women and ten for children in Maud and Maud Children's Wards, under the care of Messrs Wright and Strange.

In the late 1950s, the school for the children, which had fallen into desuetude, was recommenced. There were still children who needed prolonged treatment although fewer of them were suffering from tuberculosis, the majority now having such orthopaedic conditions as congenital dislocation of the hip, Perthes' Disease or slipped epiphysis, the two latter being non-infective hip disorders specific to children up to the age of puberty. Talipes, or foot deformities, and scoliosis, curvature of the spine, were also conditions which demanded prolonged treatment, as did the sequelae of poliomyelitis and spastic paralyses. These children had to be treated during the years when they would normally be receiving their education and the provision of educational facilities was an essential part of the hospital's work.

Originally the teaching was in the wards but the Thanet Education Committee, who supplied the teachers, proposed, on 26th April 1968, and went on to build, an excellent school with two rooms which could be used for different ages of children at the same time (C & T DHA Doc.22). The work later extended to older children and even adults, who were able to use the facilities for occupational therapy and vocational training in commercial activities such as typing. Two other groups of children who were able to benefit from the advantages of a secluded hospital school were certain girls who became pregnant during their early and middle 'teens and were adjudged unsuitable for attendance at normal schools and some children with asthma.

When Mr Strange started working regularly at the Royal Sea Bathing Hospital, he enquired of Mrs Hardy, Dr Armstrong's excellent secretary, whether there had been any cases of sacro-iliac tuberculosis treated at the hospital. He had been interested in the subject for many years and had written an article on it in conjunction with Mr (later Sir) Herbert Seddon in 1940. So superb were Dr Armstrong's indexing and storage systems that Mrs Hardy was able to produce, within a very few days, some 200 cases, fully documented, going back to 1922, together with their X-rays, for his examination. 150 of these were considered to be suitable for inclusion in a study which Mr Strange subsequently published in 1963. What a commentary this is on the present-day situation when all X-rays are destroyed within five years of the patient's discharge from treatment!

There is, of course, another side to the question. In former times, the X-ray films were inflammable and it is also a tribute to the storage methods in use at the hospital that no harm came.

However, at a date in the 1970s, possibly when storage conditions had changed, certain batches of X-ray films in storage actually underwent spontaneous combustion and even exploded! Their removal necessitated the use of asbestos gloves by the men called in to dispose of them!

With the increasing work, additional appointments to the staff of the Royal Sea Bathing Hospital became necessary. Dr Thierens was the Radiologist and served for many years but was replaced on his retirement by Dr Cant in 1958. Dr Forsaith was appointed as Consultant Anaesthetist in 1952 but was greatly missed when he subsequently handed over certain of his duties to Dr Roger Kirkpatrick who lived, much more conveniently, in Thanet. Dr Kirkpatrick took over the work with enthusiasm and was always in the forefront of anaesthetic advances. Thenceforward, Dr Forsaith limited his work to the Canterbury area as he lived just outside the city.

Dr Peter Read, Consultant Anaesthetist, came on the staff when the non-tuberculous work started in 1952 and later, Dr M.M. Voysey, in 1962. She herself came from Jamaica in the West Indies and continued the high traditions of the hospital originated by that other native of the Caribbean, John Coakley Lettsom. After many years as Consultant Anaesthetist, she transferred her interests to administration, continuing her strong personal interest in the Royal Sea Bathing Hospital.

Chapter 12
STAFFING AND TRAINING

In February 1952 Her Majesty, Queen Elizabeth II acceded to the throne and on 28th June the hospital was informed by the Group Secretary, Mr Brown, that Her Majesty had granted her patronage to the Royal Sea Bathing Hospital (RSBHA 428/9). Unfortunately, it has not been possible to retrieve the original letter from the Palace but it is hoped that it will ultimately be found.

Dr Armstrong actually retired in 1954 after a life devoted to all aspects of the welfare of the Royal Sea Bathing Hospital and, of course, to every one of his patients in every conceivable detail. After a relatively short retirement, Dr Armstrong died in 1958. So was lost a man who had stamped his personality on the hospital in a very particular manner. His enthusiasm, his devotion and his attention to every problem, no matter how small, in the care of his patients, their well-being and their psychological mileau, meant that the Royal Sea Bathing Hospital achieved the high level of morale and loyalty among both patients and staff which is its particular characteristic. A plaque was raised as a memorial to Dr Armstrong in the hospital chapel.

A further extension of the orthopaedic facilities was made in 1954 when Lettsom Ward was opened for ten male orthopaedic patients. With such a broad spectrum of orthopaedics developing in the hospital, it became recognised for the Orthopaedic Nursing Certificate (ONC) and was to have, over the years, an extremely high pass rate for this diploma. Several nurses gained Distinction in the final examination and there were three or four who were placed in the top five in the country in different years.

Such a school was a distinct help in nursing recruitment as nurses could, originally, start at the age of seventeen on this course and the two-year course counted as one year of the general nursing training. This changed gradually as the General Nursing Council placed more and more obstacles in the path of the Special Hospitals and gradually eliminated the Special Nursing Certificates. The first step was to reduce the value of the two years' training to six months and later to eliminate it altogether.

Again, it was laid down in the following decade that seventeen-year-old girls could only work in children's wards. This naturally curtailed their usefulness and could be interpreted as an insult to the maturity of seventeen-year-olds, though it was really more of an additional restrictive practice.

Certainly no harm was ever apparent in the girls before this stipulation came into force. However, for many years in the 1950s, 1960s and 1970s we

ISLE OF THANET HOSPITAL MANAGEMENT COMMITTEE

Memorandum

From: Secretary   My Ref. S/P/11/JI

To: Hospital Secretary,
       Royal Sea Bathing Hospital

Royal Patronage

Will you please inform your House Committee at their next
meeting that Her Majesty The Queen has been graciously pleased
to grant her Patronage to the Royal Sea Bathing Hospital.

It will be in order for the words "Patron - Her Majesty
The Queen" to appear in future under the name of your hospital
on all correspondence.

28th June, 1952   Secretary

Notification of Her Majesty Queen Elizabeth II's Patronage of the Royal Sea Bathing Hospital on 28th June 1952.

enjoyed the service provided by these nurses and the challenge of their training.

One of the factors that affected the nursing staff of the Royal Sea Bathing Hospital was that the NHS brought in general rules applying equally to hospitals of widely differing characteristics. The Royal Sea Bathing Hospital, over the years, had had excellent systems of affiliation for nursing training with a number of other hospitals, some of which have already been mentioned. To remind readers, these at this time included St Thomas' Hospital, The Radcliffe Infirmary at Oxford and the Hertford County Hospital, amongst others. Shortly before the war the Board had recorded: "Practically no difficulty has been experienced at this hospital in attracting a sufficient number of probationers" (Reports 1938). But these arrangements did not fit in with those of the NHS and so were lost with the consequent increasing difficulty of recruiting nursing staff which has been a prominent factor in recent years.

When the Royal Sea Bathing Hospital started to take in non-tuberculous patients, there was always a doubt in those patients' minds that they might contract tuberculosis in the hospital, for it was widely known throughout the Isle of Thanet what purpose the hospital served: or at least, what purpose it had served and was, as far as they knew, still serving. Each patient had to be individually reassured when put on the waiting-list for the Royal Sea Bathing Hospital and gradually the prejudice was worn down. It took some years for this, but as the number of tuberculous cases fell away so sharply, and as more people came safely through a stay in the hospital, the doubts and anxieties disappeared.

An important development in orthopaedic management and training was begun in the middle 1950s. A weekly half session was put aside for a clinical conference. Up to three selected patients were brought up for examination where they presented aspects of orthopaedics which were either problems of diagnosis or treatment or of particular interest or represented an important experience for the junior members of the orthopaedic staff. Apart from the advantage to them of the teaching that arose out of these sessions, a tremendous advantage accrued to the patient, for a second or third consultant opinion became available within the ambit of the NHS and, of course, at no expense to him or her. The discussions that were provoked invariably helped the surgeon in charge of the case, either to obtain confirmation of his views or to be presented with alternative appraisals which were very often most helpful.

These meetings, which were attended by all members of the orthopaedic team unless unavoidably prevented, were also open to the nurses studying for their ONC. No attempt was made to "talk down" to them even though they were quite junior, or to stop and explain technical language. They undoubtedly absorbed Orthopaedics "through the pores", as one might say, and the high level of achievement in the ONC examinations that resulted has already been mentioned.

These conferences alternated for many years with the Kent & Canterbury Hospital until, in the middle 1980s, they were limited to the latter hospital. While this was unfortunately necessary, the impact was mollified to some extent by the discontinuation of the ONC, so that it was not missed as much as otherwise it might have been. The junior orthopaedic staff, when possible, travelled to Canterbury to take part in the conferences and the new venue also allowed junior staff from the William Harvey Hospital at Ashford to take part.

The National Health Service had many different effects on the medical services of the country, not all of them good, even though its broad aim was resoundingly achieved. One serious aspect was the loss, by all the Voluntary Hospitals that were taken over, of their private funds which were, in many cases, considerable. These monies were passed to the Regional Hospital Boards.

Boards of Governors were disbanded and, in the case of the Royal Sea Bathing Hospital, this meant that not only did it lose a very large sum of money but it lost its connection with the London Committee. The formation of the League of Friends did something to recompense the hospital for the loss of its private fortune but the League could only operate locally and so never had access to the large sources of charitable donation that were available to the London Committee. A certain amount of so-called "free money" was given back to the hospital by the Regional Board but overall the hospital lost heavily at a time when it badly needed the money for rebuilding.

In fact, it never received a vote towards rebuilding in the ensuing forty years and did not even receive a sufficient annual budget to keep it in repair with the result that it gradually became more and more delapidated. Only the action of the League of Friends in the late 1980s repaired one feature that had become a complete disgrace.

Another important result of the formation of the NHS was that the hospital became simply a part of a Hospital Management Group under the Isle of Thanet Hospital Management Committee. Its needs, therefore, could no longer be considered in isolation but only in relation to the needs of the Group as a whole. This was particularly noticeable when a new operating theatre became necessary. Set against this was the need for a new medical ward at the Margate Wing of the Isle of Thanet District General Hospital (as it was called) and the Royal Sea Bathing Hospital lost the battle.

There is little doubt that the London Committee, in the old days, would have come up with the money at once!

Chapter 13
THE OLD OPERATING THEATRE

With the increasing number of orthopaedic patients passing through the Royal Sea Bathing Hospital and the increasing number of beds becoming available to them, the orthopaedic stature of the hospital grew. As early as 1959, only seven years after the first non-tuberculous patient was admitted, the British Orthopaedic Association chose to send down only the third group of American and Canadian Travelling Fellows to Canterbury and Thanet as part of their Travelling Fellowship, enabling them to see British Orthopaedics for themselves.

Mr Strange had had the good fortune to have been one of the first group of British Travelling Fellows to visit orthopaedic centres in USA and Canada in 1948. From this original expedition there developed an annual reciprocal visit from both sides of the Atlantic which also included young orthopaedic surgeons from Australia, New Zealand, South Africa and Canada as well as from USA and Britain. This has proved of inestimable value in cementing relations and fostering the spread of orthopaedic knowledge throughout the English-speaking world. The Royal Sea Bathing Hospital has taken part in this work on several occasions since, hosting the visits of the Travelling Fellows on four occasions during the following twenty-eight years.

These comprise four or five young American and one or two young Canadian orthopaedic surgeons who come to Britain in years alternate to British Commonwealth Surgeons' visits to North American orthopaedic centres.

One of the features that the Travelling Fellows particularly enjoyed was taking part in one of the weekly staff clinical conferences at the Royal Sea Bathing Hospital. At these, they could see patients and participate in the discussions themselves, incidentally adding considerably to their value, rather than just sitting and being lectured at, which had tended to be the pattern in some of the other centres they visited.

It may be noted that they represent (and the word is used in the present tense because these exchanges are continuing) the very cream of New World Orthopaedic Surgeons, selected from a huge and highly competitive field. It is all the more honour to the Royal Sea Bathing Hospital that it should be chosen to receive them and show them some of the work of the hospital as representative of English orthopaedic surgery.

153

Visit of the British Orthopaedic Association to The Royal Sea Bathing Hospital, May 1962.

Naturally, men of such potential achieve great heights in the sphere of orthopaedics and as time goes on, number among them Presidents of the American and Canadian Orthopaedic Associations, the American Academy of Orthopaedic Surgeons, editors of the American Issue of the Journal of Bone and Joint Surgery and of Campbell's "Operative Orthopaedics".

Further development of the orthopaedic work of the Royal Sea Bathing Hospital and its growing reputation led Mr (later Sir) Frank Holdsworth, President of the British Orthopaedic Association, to make the request, in the autumn of 1961, that the Royal Sea Bathing Hospital should host the Spring Meeting of the Association the following April. Naturally the honour of such a request made it complied with as a command with delight and great preparations were put in train to ensure that the meeting would be a success.

About 150 orthopaedic surgeons from all over Britain attended and an extensive display of clinical cases was presented for discussion by Messrs Strange and Wright, assisted by Mr R.C. Baird of Ashford. The Mayor and Corporation of Margate gave a reception for the Association and the meeting was universally acclaimed an unqualified success.

Amongst some of the other distinguished orthopaedic surgeons who have visited the Royal Sea Bathing Hospital of recent years have been many Presidents of the British Orthopaedic Association, Presidents of the Australian, Canadian and South African Associations, the Editors of the British Issue of the Journal of Bone and Joint Surgery and of Watson-Jones' "Fractures and Joint Injuries" and distinguished orthopaedic surgeons from many other countries. In short, the Royal Sea Bathing Hospital has a reputation in the sphere of orthopaedics worldwide, comparable with the reputation it had nationwide in former days.

Not only so, but in the early 1950s, the hospital was visited by a Russian doctor from the Crimea to observe the treatment of tuberculosis at this hospital.

It may be difficult to appreciate quite how close to the sea the Royal Sea Bathing Hospital is situated. The northern end of Erasmus Wilson's ward block extends right to the edge of the low cliff above the promenade. The photograph taken in the 1960s shows Westbrook Bay as seen from the roof of Alexandra Ward. This view is the one which would have been seen by patients on Alexandra Ward balcony as they took the sun and air as depicted in the colour supplement.

The operating theatre, which was built in 1905, had many important features. In the first place, it was very large compared with the usual size of operating theatres. In one corner was the steam sterilizing unit and on the north face, a window that occupied half the wall.

Right up until the early 1960s, the effect of having such an excellent theatre was that infection of surgical wounds was quite exceptional and "clean" orthopaedic operations could be undertaken without fear of infection. In fact, the average infection rate was well below that laid down as 0.8 per cent by Jackson Burroughs, Consulting Orthopaedic Surgeon at St Bartholomew's Hospital, a former President of the British Orthopaedic Association but, alas, with us no longer.

Three factors contributed to this excellent record and the size of the theatre was certainly one, virtually eliminating the risk of accidental contamination of sterile operating fields. Another was that the theatre was only used for four or five half days a week. Thirdly, there were no emergency operations performed in this theatre.

Until well after the Second World War, the main anaesthetic agent was ether but in spite of that, although electricity had been installed in 1910, the emergency lighting was by gas. In 1936 Miss Harcourt was Theatre Sister and, now Mrs Francis, she recalls how it became necessary, on two occasions, to use the emergency illumination, pulling down the four little rings on chains to light the gas mantles. No harm came, even though the anaesthetics being administered were open ether. Of course, this also infers that the pilot lights for these gas lights were burning all the time, ether or no!

In fact, there were gas fires in the plaster room next door, where the acetone-dissolved celluloid on the plaster beds was being dried and, in the next room which was the sister's office, the anaesthetic store was in a cupboard only a few feet from her open coal fire.

It may be that Dr Armstrong's view, that the steam sterilizing in the theatre moistened the atmosphere sufficiently to prevent anaesthetic explosions, was justified. So perhaps his concern, when the sterilizing was moved out of the theatre, can be understood. However, when the alterations were carried out, ether was already in process of being replaced by non-inflammable anaesthetics, so that the risk of a tragedy was not increased.

At this time, autoclaves were installed in an adjoining room which also served as an instrument store and "laying-up" room. An anaesthetic room and a dental room were equipped and improvements made in the "scrubbing-up" facilities.

A large, highly manoeuvrable, shadowless theatre light was fitted and a modern orthopaedic operating table, the "Shropshire Horse", was purchased, no doubt at a price which would have been one tenth of that if it were bought today.

The position of the theatre was such that its huge "picture" window gave directly onto the lawns of the hospital and onto the North Sea not fifty yards away. It was high enough above the ground as not to need to be frosted and, in consequence, provided a magnificent view, as shown in the colour supplement.

In fine summer weather there could be seen from this window the "Queen of the Channel" or the "Royal Daffodil", gleaming white, sizeable steamships, coming into Margate to take holidaymakers to France or Southend. The sands were crowded with bathers and sun-bathers and there were pedal boats, speedboats, water skiers and yachts. In the winter Mr Wright's ornithological eye would be refreshed by descrying skeins of Brent or Barnacle geese flying over from their feeding grounds at Sheerness or Sheppey and waders and migrants breaking their journey at Margate at the change of the seasons.

It is true that one day in the winter of 1962/63 the sea suddenly appeared completely covered with ice for some miles out from the shore. However, it was not Margate's ice but ice from Whitstable where the Thames estuary shelves very gradually, so that for several miles out the sea is only a foot or two deep. It was here that the sea actually froze to a thickness of about eight inches of ice. With the change of the tides and the currents, this ice was floated down to Margate, which explains the suddenness of the appearance of frozen sea outside the window one morning to catch the eye of the operating surgeon.

The relief a surgeon experiences by lifting up his eyes, if not to the hills, at least to the horizon, from having been concentrating on an operating field only inches from his face for long periods, can only be experienced to be understood. Unfortunately, there must be very few surgeons who have been lucky enough to experience it. Every single surgeon who has visited the Royal Sea Bathing Hospital's theatre, and there have been hundreds of them from all over the globe, has exclaimed, without exception, his jealousy of the surgeons at the Royal Sea Bathing Hospital for being able to work in such a delightful theatre.

Orthopaedic Nursing Conference, 1965.

Association of Superintendent Chartered Physiotherapists' Spring Conference, 1973.

Chapter 14
VISITS OF PROFESSIONAL ASSOCIATIONS

As has been mentioned, Dr Kirkpatrick and Miss Voysey were Consultant Anaesthetists to the Royal Sea Bathing Hospital and latterly were joined by Dr Kulasinghe. With increasing surgical work, further anaesthetic appointments became necessary, and they were joined by Drs Ferguson, Makel, Lewin and Proctor, though they had other assignments in the Isle of Thanet as well. Mr Burdett was appointed as Hospital Secretary in 1951. He served in a most loyal way and always had the welfare of the hospital, patients and staff at heart. This may in some way have been more natural to him than to some as he himself had a long-standing physical disability which he never allowed to interfere with his duties. When he retired in 1983, after 32 years' service, he took over the duties of secretary to the League of Friends of the hospital. He was followed as Hospital Secretary by Mr Belcher.

With the increasing shortage of nurses, and the greater number of nurses living at home, some of the accommodation in the nurses' home was converted to house very necessary offices.

From 1953 onwards many societies visited the Royal Sea Bathing Hospital for their meetings; these included the British Association of Orthopaedic Nurses who visited twice, the National Association of Theatre Nurses, the Association of Superintendent Physiotherapists, the Irish Institute of Orthopaedics and others.

Certain visits of important national societies need recording in greater detail. For example, in 1966, when Mr Strange was President of the Orthopaedic Section of the Royal Society of Medicine, the section held its annual "Country Meeting" at the Royal Sea Bathing Hospital. Some 60 Orthopaedic Surgeons attended, amongst whom was Mr R. Weedon Butler, the Senior Orthopaedic Surgeon at Addenbrooke's Hospital, Cambridge. He was a direct descendant of the Rev. Weedon Butler who had "offered a solemn prayer that the Almighty might bless the pious and charitable undertaking" at the laying of the Foundation Stone of the Hospital in 1792. In the photograph of this meeting, Mr Butler (front row) is indicated by arrow B. The arrow D points to Mr John Dickson, Consultant Orthopaedic Surgeon at Ipswich, the son of Dr Dickson who was Resident Surgeon at the Royal Sea Bathing Hospital in 1920.

Meeting of the Medical Society of London at the Royal Sea Bathing Hospital in part celebration of its Bicentenary, 14th July 1973.

Meeting of the Orthopaedic Section of the Royal Society of Medicine under the Presidency of Mr F.G. St Clair Strange. June 4th 1966. The letter "B" indicates Mr Weedon Butler, FRCS, whose ancestor gave the prayer at the laying of the Foundation Stone. The letter "D" identifies Mr Dickson, FRCS, son of Dr Dickson who was Resident Surgeon at the Royal Sea Bathing Hospital in 1920.

1973 was the Bicentenary of the foundation, also by Dr John Coakley Lettsom, of the Medical Society of London. The Royal Sea Bathing Hospital invited the Society down to Margate so that part of its celebrations could be held at its sister establishment. So it was that, on 14th July 1973 the Medical Society of London visited the Royal Sea Bathing Hospital, under the chairmanship of one of its former Presidents, Dr "Tommy" Hunt. During the visit the Royal Sea Bathing Hospital presented the Society with an Honorific Document in commemoration of its Bicentenary. The document was written in the most beautiful calligraphy and read as follows:

"Presented to the Medical Society of London in celebration of the Bicentenary of its foundation in 1773 by John Coakley Lettsom, Quaker, Physician, Botanist, Philanthropist, Native of Tortola, by the Staff of the Royal Sea Bathing Hospital, founded by John Coakley Lettsom in 1791. 1973."

This Honorific Document was embellished by nine mint postage stamps:

Two of these showed maps of the Virgin Islands, namely, the 4c of 1951 and the $4.80 of 1952. The ½c of 1951 and the 70c of 1964 showed maps of Tortola.

Five stamps were issued in 1973 commemorating the Bicentenary of the Medical Society of London and the persuasion of the Quakers:

The ½c shows a portrait of Lettsom, the facsimile of his signature and his dates: 1744-1815. Birthplace, the British Virgin Islands. Medical Society of London, founded by John Coakley Lettsom.

The 10c shows Lettsom House, the Medical Society of London, founded AD 1773, with the Lettsom Medal superimposed. John Coakley Lettsom, birthplace, the British Virgin Islands.

161

The 15c shows William Thornton and the Capitol Building in Washington, DC, which was built to his design as winner of the prize which had been offered for its architecture.

The 30c shows William Thornton and the Library Hall, Philadelphia which he also designed. Thornton was a relative of Lettsom.

The $1.00 shows William Penn, Founder of Pennsylvania.

They were all Quakers.

In return, Dr Tommy Hunt, on behalf of the Medical Society of London, presented to the Royal Sea Bathing Hospital a History of the Medical Society of London, written by himself (RSBHA 414).

After a tour of the hospital and an exhibition of historical relics, a short talk on the history of the hospital was given to the members of the Medical Society of London, which demonstrated, amongst other things, the close relationship that existed between the Society and the Royal Sea Bathing Hospital.

As part of its celebrations, the Medical Society of London had invited the Senior Surgeon of the Royal Sea Bathing Hospital, Mr Strange, to represent the hospital at the society's Bicentenary Banquet in London on 16th May 1973. At this he was accompanied by his daughter, Dr Diana Khursandi, MA, BM, B.Ch., FFARCS.

A distressing incident occurred in 1973 when the Matron, Miss Birks, was taking her driving test. As she got out of the car at the end of the test, she suffered a fatal heart attack.

Mr Reg Jones, the orthopaedic surgeon, who was working in the Canterbury and South-East Kent Groups, was an essential member of the East Kent team although he had no sessions at the Royal Sea Bathing Hospital. However, he accompanied Mr Strange, Mr Wright and Mr Klugman across the Channel by Hovercraft from Pegwell Bay on 26th April 1974 to visit the famous Institut Calot at Berck-Plage in the Pas de Calais. Prof. Jean Cauchoix and the staff of the Institut presented papers and gave us much food for thought and, after luncheon, Prof. Cauchoix demonstrated his operation for leg lengthening, a remarkable operation, although none of the Royal Sea Bathing Hospital's staff felt disposed to copy it. We were also shown the programme for the treatment of scoliosis, with a special technique of self-operated spinal traction.

While the outward journey had been so rough that it was at the maximum the hovercraft was designed for, the weather for the return journey was worse, so that we had to come home by the ferry as the hovercraft could not face the worsening storm. Happily, a return visit by members of the orthopaedic staff of the Institut Calot to the Royal Sea Bathing Hospital was arranged for 24th October 1975. This was blessed with rather more clement weather and a needle match of boules was played against them in the quadrangle of the Royal Sea Bathing Hospital. History does not record the result!

A concert in the chapel followed and was designed, by Mr Glyn Thomas, to include excerpts from Mendelsohn's Elijah and other works chosen to display in as contemporary a way as possible the acoustic qualities of this lovely example of "Victorian Gothic" church building.

Amongst the guests from the Institut Calot were Drs Coursou, Heripret, Duriez, Morel, Mounier-Kuhn and Cauchoix. Unfortunately Dr Cottrell was unable to come. As has been mentioned previously, such occasions are often marked with a "sumptuous entertainment"! While the meal that evening was not, perhaps, quite one to deserve such an epithet, an attempt was made to provide as English a meal as possible for our French guests.

MENU

Cream of Tomato Soup with Croutons
or Chilled Melon

Roast Beef
Yorkshire Pudding   Horseradish Sauce
or
Cold Gammon Salad
Roast Potatoes   Cauliflower Polonaise
Duchesse Potatoes   Buttered Carrots

Apple Pie and Ice Cream
or
Sherry Trifle
Fresh Cream

Selection of English Cheeses
Biscuits

Coffee

Beer   Squash

One of the highlights of 1974 occurred when the Medical Society of London presented to the Royal Sea Bathing Hospital the original letter from the Prince Regent to Dr Lettsom in which the Prince recorded his vote in the election of a resident surgeon in 1812. This has been already described and illustrated in chapter 2 and constitutes, as may well be imagined, one of the most treasured additions to the archives of the hospital.

In 1976 the British Orthopaedic Association was host to the Sixth Combined Meeting of the Orthopaedic Associations of the English-Speaking World. This met in London but, on its conclusion, six Post-Conference Tours were organised for the delegates to visit other centres of orthopaedics. One of these tours came to Margate and visited the Royal Sea Bathing Hospital. Again, in 1980, when the British Orthopaedic Association held its Spring Meeting in Canterbury, a similar group of orthopaedic

163

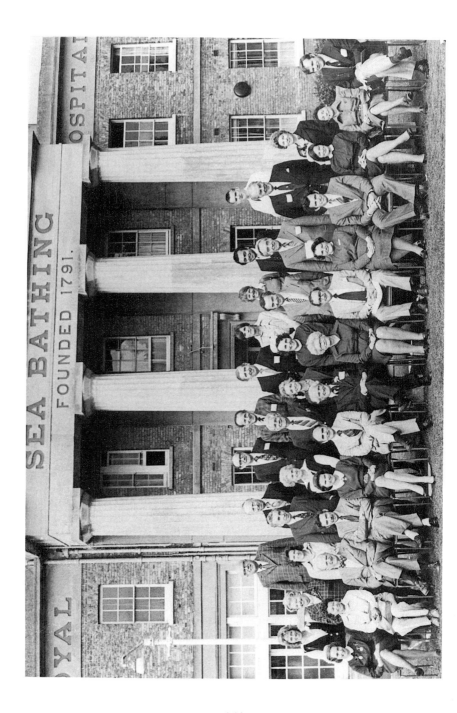

164

Opposite: Post-Conference Tour visiting the hospital after the 6th Combined Meeting of the Orthopaedic Associations of the English-Speaking World, 22nd September 1976.

Back row, l to r: Dr Holman, New Jersey, USA (since deceased); Dr Albert, Pennsylvania, USA; Dr Crenshaw, Tennessee, USA (Editor, Campbell's Operative Orthopaedics); Dr Bryer, Johannesburg, Republic of South Africa; Dr Sutherland, South Australia, Australia; Mrs Soper, California, USA; Mrs Glockner, Massachusetts, USA; Dr Hague, Royal Sea Bathing Hospital; Mr Austin, Royal Sea Bathing Hospital.

Middle row: Mrs Glyn Thomas, Royal Sea Bathing Hospital; Mrs Holman, New Jersey, USA; Mrs Hazlett, Ontario, Canada; Mr Wright, Royal Sea Bathing Hospital; Mrs Albert, Pennsylvania, USA; Dr Siegling, South Carolina, USA; Mrs Crenshaw, Tennessee, USA; Sister Mack, Royal Sea Bathing Hospital; Mr Glyn Thomas, Royal Sea Bathing Hospital (later President, Orthopaedic Section, RSM and Hon. Sec. British Orthopaedic Association); Dr Coates, South Australia, Australia; Dr Hazlett, Ontario, Canada (later, President, Canadian Orthopaedic Association); Mrs Papademetriou, New York, USA.

Front row: Sister Carmichael, Royal Sea Bathing Hospital; Mrs Marsh, Kansas, USA; Mr Jones, Royal Sea Bathing Hospital; Mrs Stevens, Nursing Officer, Royal Sea Bathing Hospital; Dr Papademetriou, New York, USA; Mr Strange, Royal Sea Bathing Hospital (Past President, Orthopaedic Section, RSM & Past Vice-President, British Orthopaedic Association); Mrs Siegling, South Carolina, USA; Dr Glockner, Massachusetts, USA; Sister Stidwell, Royal Sea Bathing Hospital; Mr Klugman, Royal Sea Bathing Hospital; Sister Banks, Royal Sea Bathing Hospital; Mrs Wright, Royal Sea Bathing Hospital; Dr Soper, California, USA.

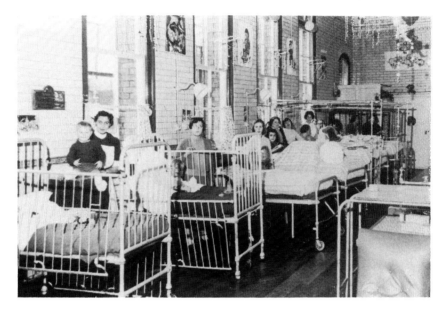

Children's Ward with Sister Wilbourne.

surgeons and their wives visited the Royal Sea Bathing Hospital. As these visitors came from all corners of the globe, the reputation of the hospital was consequently spread world-wide and it is sad that, as will be seen in a later chapter, a hospital of such character should be facing the end of its independent life.

In 1965 Mr T. Glyn Thomas, FRCS, was appointed as Consultant Orthopaedic Surgeon in East Kent, based on Dover. He always attended the weekly Orthopaedic Staff Conferences and, soon after his arrival, inaugurated the monthly Orthopaedic Residents' Club. This was an evening meeting held at one or other of the hospitals in East Kent, including the Royal Sea Bathing Hospital, for the benefit of the junior orthopaedic staff. It became customary for nurses working in various spheres of orthopaedics in the several hospitals in East Kent to attend these meetings as well, so that the name naturally became altered to the East Kent Orthopaedic Club. In the days of the ONC the nurses taking the course also attended with great advantage to their grip of orthopaedics.

These meetings were usually preceded by a buffet supper which was invariably provided by the generosity of one of the drug or surgical instrument companies associated with the hospitals in East Kent.

Mr Thomas went on to become the Honorary Secretary of the British Orthopaedic Association in 1980-81 and President of the Orthopaedic

166

Section of the Royal Society of Medicine in 1984-85 and held an important honorary position in the Medical Protection Society.

By now a very great change in the pattern of orthopaedics was taking place. Tuberculosis had virtually disappeared, anterior poliomyelitis was disappearing under the influence of the Salk vaccine and acute infections of bones and joints were becoming rare owing to the improved living standards and the effect of the antibiotic drugs. Congenital dislocation of the hip was being diagnosed at the neo-natal stage when its treatment could be undertaken as an out-patient and Perthes' Disease of the hip demanded much less time in hospital. In consequence of these factors, long-stay beds were being turned over to short-stay problems.

However, two other trends were becoming apparent. More people fractured the neck of the femur on account of the increased longevity of the population and the long periods spent by older people sitting in front of the television instead of maintaining the health of their bones by leading a more physically active life.

The second factor was the very widespread condition of osteo-arthritis, particularly in the hip, due again to the ageing of the population.

When non-tuberculous orthopaedic work started at the Royal Sea Bathing Hospital, the treatment for osteo-arthritis of the hip in the elderly was a high femoral osteotomy, described by McMurray of Liverpool in 1935. This realigned the bone and caused the tissues to undertake repair in such a way that the arthritic process was arrested, often for several years.

But Smith-Petersen, of Boston, had been working on his Vitallium Mold Arthroplasty of the hip and Mr Strange, after having visited Smith-Petersen at the Massachusetts General Hospital and seen him do his operation, was in process of introducing it in East Kent. The operation was to insert a non-corrosive metallic cup into the hip and the method had some disadvantages as well as many successes.

However, the operation was being superceded by the "Acrylic Head" of the Judet Brothers, Lagrange and Dunoyer (1954). This also gave brilliant results but sadly, the benefit seldom lasted longer than three years. These were the first operations for hip reconstruction undertaken at the Royal Sea Bathing Hospital but happily further progress was to follow.

Austin Moore's "self-locking" hip prosthesis was the next step and was quickly followed by Thompson's which was not self-locking but also worked well as a replacement for the ball of the ball-in-socket hip joint.

But total joint replacement was coming in. Pioneered by McKee of Norwich (1951) and Charnley of Wrightington (1961), they laid the pattern for hip surgery for the next thirty years and modifications of their original operations are performed around the world in their thousands every week and weekly in the Royal Sea Bathing Hospital.

167

Other advances of which full advantage is taken at the Royal Sea Bathing Hospital are osteotomy and joint replacement for arthritis of the knee and endoscopy of the joints, that is, examining the interior of joints through a very slim telescope so that diagnosis may be made by direct vision without having to open the joint up fully.

Another sphere in which modern methods are employed is in the treatment of curvature of the spine. A high degree of correction may now be obtained and lengthy periods of traction in bed are things of the past.

All hospitals have great festivities at Christmas and the Royal Sea Bathing Hospital is no exception in this respect. As well as the late night tour of the wards by the nurses and other helpers singing carols on Christmas Eve, there is the traditional decorating of the wards that afternoon.

On one Christmas Eve afternoon in the early 1970s, there was a rather old lady in Louise Ward who was not at all well. After lunch, she fell asleep. During the afternoon, the ward was decorated by the nurses and the theme was angels and cherubs. These had been beautifully drawn on thin card and coloured and cut out and were suspended in different positions and at different heights around the ward. Presently the old lady awoke and let out an ear-piercing shriek: she thought that she must have died and woken up in heaven!

Although this story was told to me by the sister of the ward at the time, Mrs Stevens, she did not relate whether the old lady was pleased or not at finding that she had only woken up in this world after all!

This story is a remarkable parallel to the one told in chapter nine about the wounded soldier from Dunkirk who woke up in the chapel.

From 1969 onwards East Kent became one of the spheres of rotation of the Senior Orthopaedic Registrar training scheme, the rotation being one year at King's College Hospital, one year at Bromley, one year in East Kent and a further year at King's. This meant that the Royal Sea Bathing Hospital gained from their services and at the same time, played its part in giving them the training and experience needed to equip them for Consultant posts.

In the years that followed, every Senior Orthopaedic Registrar trained in this way achieved a Consultant appointment with the exception of one in 1988 who decided to take a year in Australia as part of his further education. One, indeed, had taken up a Consultant post in Australia, namely Jim Curtiss, at Cairns in Queensland although, sadly, he subsequently had to give up the post owing to ill health and transferred to Brisbane.

It is an example of the quality of the Senior Registrars who have passed through this training that two of them have been considered the best in strong fields of applicants for Consultant Orthopaedic posts in East Kent and E.R.L. Jones and Martin Lock have become active members of the

East Kent Orthopaedic Unit, Reg Jones since 1970 and Martin Lock since 1986. David Klugman also joined the staff through the King's rotation in 1973 but, having had part of his post-graduate training and experience in South Africa, was actually appointed before he was due to join the East Kent year of the rotation.

Other orthopaedic surgeons have been appointed to the staff from other centres, namely Martin Conybeare from Oxford, Ian Stephen from Exeter and Nigel Blackburn from Windsor and the Royal Free Hospital. In this way any risk of parochialism is eliminated, although such is the standard of our locally trained men that there have been no worries in this context.

Mr Conybeare, Mr Stephen and Mr Blackburn, as well as Mr Klugman, all have active connections with the Royal Sea Bathing Hospital and its orthopaedic staff continues its long-standing traditions.

The orthopaedic bed strength was maintained in the region of one hundred beds in the late 1980s although parts of the KG Wards were taken out of service. They had been renamed in recognition of the services of Basil Armstrong, Olive Monahan and St Clair Strange but the old names of the KG Wards had been in service for so long that the new names were very slow in coming into general use.

However, as financial stringency has affected every branch of the National Health Service for so many years, the orthopaedic bed strength continues to be pruned and, at the end of the 1980s, barely exceeds 50.

Chapter 15

"MARGATE AIR"

During the period of the late 1960s and early 1970s various structural alterations were made. These included enclosing many of the balconies with brick and glass and supplying heating. Hot house plants began to be raised where snow used to fall and North Sea gales used to sweep the balconies and keep them fresh and clean. Erasmus Wilson's comment on the "sweetness" of the wards a hundred years earlier was becoming superceded, although his earlier suggestion that "some charitably disposed person" should heat the wards was becoming fulfilled. However, Lettsom's "solaria" were now largely things of the past. No longer did sparrows nest in the balconies or seagulls come onto the patients' beds at meal times for their regular supply of scraps. But staphylococci found that the balconies were no longer a hostile terrain and wounds became more liable to infection again. Part of the balcony of Victoria (children's) Ward was glassed in at this time when Perthes' Disease of the hip was treated by balanced traction in Balkan beams. But sadly the doors onto the balcony were made too low for the beams to traverse and so the then longest-stay patients were denied the benefits of the open air. In these days of central administration one might be forgiven for thinking that it would do no harm, rather good, if a certain degree of consultation between the users of hospital facilities and their designers were allowed or even encouraged.

In part rectification of these enclosures, at least for the benefit of some of the staff, Mr Strange, after doing a weekly ward round in Armstrong Ward, the boys' ward above Maud, used to take his Senior House Officer and Registrar and his secretary along the open top of the Erasmus Wilson block to the very end, overlooking the sea not twenty yards away. This little ritual, carried out in all weathers, ensured, Mr Strange averred, that three breaths of Margate air once a week was a sure prevention of all the ills that the lungs were heir to! This contention has, to date, neither been proved nor disproved but, at least, it underlined Lettsom's assessment of "the extreme salubrity of that part of the coast". We can ignore the late Tommy Cooper's quip, when told "Margate is good for rheumatism" that he went there and got it (Madden 1989).

As the National Health Service gradually became more administratively tidy, Hospital Management Committees, and — their later title — District Health Authorities, started to refuse to pay for patients from one area to be treated in another or to treat patients from other areas. This meant that some of the special facilities of the Royal Sea Bathing Hospital were denied to some who might have benefited from them and, in particular, those who lived in the adjoining area of the South-East Kent District. This was especially unfortunate because those patients were under the treatment of members of the Orthopaedic Department of East Kent who had, in some instances, actual sessions at the Royal Sea Bathing Hospital but were unable to treat their own patients there. It also meant, of course, that the hospital was no longer a National, nor even a Regional Centre and part of its unique character down the centuries was lost. For example, in the census of 1841 (Whyman, l.c.) it was noted that out of 214 patients only nine were born in Kent, 204 came from other counties and one even came from Ireland!

With the development of equal opportunities for the sexes, more men came into nursing, many of whom reached the upper levels of nursing administration. It therefore became no longer possible to address the head nurse of a hospital as Matron if it happened to be a man. Nurses were therefore regraded by numbers and the head nurse of the Royal Sea Bathing Hospital became a "Number Seven"! Amongst these were Mrs Notcutt, who had been Sister (a now obsolete title) of one of the KG Wards for many years, and who filled the post with great good humour, and Mrs Stevens, whose friendly personality, coupled with her ability to command absolute discipline without in any way alienating the staff, resulted in the highest rate of nursing recruitment the hospital had known in recent years.

Fortunately more reasonable attitudes in the later 1980s discontinued the numerical description of nursing staff and more realistic nomenclature was re-established. Of course, it is still the case that if visiting hospitals in the United States, it is wise to remember that addressing the nurse in charge of a ward as "Sister" is likely to be taken to assume that you are getting "fresh"!

But attention must be directed to more serious things. An event very closely associated with the Royal Sea Bathing Hospital was the sad death of Her Royal Highness Princess Alice, Countess of Athlone, on 3rd January 1981. Throughout her long life, and she lived to reach the age of 94, the longest-lived of any member of the Royal Family, she retained an active personal interest in the Royal Sea Bathing Hospital. One of the features of the National Health Service is that this form of association seems to have disappeared. Of course, Her Majesty the Queen continues to be the patron of the hospital but even this happy situation may not be long continued with the administrative plans to discontinue the hospital and incorporate the work in the Margate General Hospital.

However, at the time of writing, there seems to be no definite date yet in view, although the hospital has suffered the threat of closure for a number of years now. This can hardly be expected to raise morale but, in spite of it, the morale of the hospital continues at a very high level amongst both patients and staff.

Talking of the staff recalls the days when there was a colony of semi-wild cats in one of the basements of the hospital. Several attempts were made to get rid of them as they caused various nuisances. First of all they were confined so that they might be restricted in the damage they did and so that their food might be "doctored", but the night staff used to release them and feed them, even in the face of dire threats! In consequence, they survived for a number of years. Apparently they were not only dirty and infested with vermin but were unhealthy and in the end the RSPCA had to eliminate them.

It was mentioned in the last chapter that a group of surgeons and their wives came down to Margate to see the Royal Sea Bathing Hospital after the British Orthopaedic Association's Meeting at Canterbury in 1980. This is recalled because some of the visitors again came from very far afield. Dr Paul Lipscomb, for instance, was a senior member of the staff of the famous Mayo Clinic in Rochester, Minnesota, and came with his wife, as did Dr George Dall, who came from Cape Town where he was Professor of Orthopaedic Surgery in the University of Cape Town and had been President of the South African Orthopaedic Association the previous year. Mr Gavin Green entertained the visitors on the "Father Willis" organ in the chapel. He had been Senior Registrar in East Kent before becoming Consultant Orthopaedic Surgeon at Burton-on-Trent where he had succeeded F.W.T. Davies who had held the post for the previous thirty years after having finished his training as Senior Registrar in Canterbury and at the Royal Sea Bathing Hospital also.

While the hospital no longer receives visits from the London Medical Board as it did in the old days, it is still kept on its mettle, even if this were necessary, by looking forward to visits from such eminent people. While the hospital continues to attract such visits, there is no need for it to have an "internal audit" to monitor the standard of medical and surgical care. Indeed, it is only too obvious that, were the standard to fall, such visits would cease. However, this does not mean that internal audits are neglected, even though the reason for these is really to counter subsequent allegations of negligence which are becoming not only all too common but in some cases even frivolous.

It is fashionable to attack the medical profession now-a-days but when seen from inside, the truth is that the very nature of the work dictates to those caring for others, whatever their sphere, the motive to do the best for their patient that lies within their power. Of course they are human, for otherwise they would not care, and consequently are liable to error at times. But the law and the public consider it the duty of the medical and nursing professions to be perfect. It is a hard target to live up to, but the great majority try to do so. It would seem that the staff of the Royal Sea Bathing Hospital have made over the centuries, and still continue to make, a very good attempt to reach this standard.

Not only does the hospital act as a centre for graduates to visit and learn but it also exports some of its expertise. Mr Wright made several trips to Burma to set up an Orthopaedic Training Scheme in Rangoon, the first in 1979. It was during one absence of some six months that Mr Derek Parsons undertook his locum, seconded from Professor H.J. Seddon's staff on his recommendation. No more excellent choice could have been made for, as well as being a first-class orthopaedic surgeon, Mr Parsons was one of the most beautiful technical operators it has been a pleasure to work with.

On subsequent occasions, Mr Wright changed his venue and went off to South Africa, though usually for rather shorter visits. He chose to work in hospitals that were specifically for the native races and gained a great experience of the ills and accidents that afflicted the population in the Transvaal, Natal and Malawi as well as giving those hospitals some of his knowledge and experience based on his work at the Royal Sea Bathing Hospital.

At this time Mr Martin Conybeare was appointed Consulting Orthopaedic Surgeon and divided his time between Canterbury and Margate,

Yet another visit from an orthopaedic society took place in 1986 when the Irish Institute of Orthopaedics came over to Margate to visit the Royal Sea Bathing Hospital. After touring the hospital and completing its scientific deliberations, the institute attended a concert in the chapel given by the "Innominate Singers".

The programme was entitled "Music for a Summer Evening".

"Comfort ye My People"	G.F. Handel
"Fugue in B Minor"	J.S. Bach
"On Thee each living Soul Awaits"	J. Haydn
"Laudate Dominum and Gloria", from "The Solemn Vespers"	W.A. Mozart
"Ave Verum Corpus"	W.A. Mozart

"Comfort ye" was sung by Mr Alan Green, Vicar-Choral at St Paul's Cathedral and the Trio from Haydn's "Creation" was sung by him, Mr Glyn Thomas, whose superb voice was never heard to better advantage, and Miss Sally Ardouin, daughter of Mr Alan Ardouin, Ear, Nose and Throat Surgeon at Canterbury. Sally's beautiful voice was again heard in the "Laudate Dominum and Gloria".

Mr Gavin Green again returned to Margate to play the Bach Fugue, which was also very much appreciated. In fact, the concert was received with tumultuous applause and quite rightly given a standing ovation. Naturally an "Encore" was demanded, and, equally naturally, Mr Thomas' "Innominate Singers" chose for it Handel's immortal "Hallelujah Chorus", sung, of course, to a standing audience, and which sounded absolutely wonderful in the beautiful surroundings of the hospital chapel.

Nothing could have been more appropriate than the choice of Handel's famous music because "The Messiah" was first performed in Dublin and devoted to the charity of a hospital.

One of the "Home Team" at the time was Mrs Yvonne Brown who had been a ward sister at the General Hospital in Margate when, in 1987, she was appointed Matron of the Royal Sea Bathing Hospital. She was Matron in actual fact, but had to carry the clumsy title of "Senior Nurse Manager".

Chapter 16

CHEST DISEASES, GENITO-URINARY SURGERY AND RHEUMATOLOGY

The work of the Royal Sea Bathing Hospital has always been largely orthopaedic. That is to say, it has been concerned with, originally, tuberculous infections of bones and joints, and, since tuberculosis has been eliminated, with injuries and diseases of the locomotor system. This includes muscles, tendons, ligaments, joints, bones, peripheral nerves and the spine, together with such abnormalities as disorders of posture, gait, physical deformities from birth and various paralyses.

In bygone days, tuberculous infection of glands and abdominal tuberculosis of various kinds was included in the description "Surgical Tuberculosis", to distinguish it from Pulmonary Tuberculosis, also known as Phthisis or Consumption. The Royal Sea Bathing Hospital was never intended to treat pulmonary tuberculosis and Dr Cazin (l.c. p.342) quoted the original rules: *"La phthisie n'est pas admise"*. As has already been observed, Margate is not, perhaps, the best place for such cases. However, in spite of this, many serious bone and joint infections were accompanied by involvement of the lungs and even some cases with open chest infections had to be retained. It was therefore inevitable that some patients who had quite severe lung involvement had to remain in the Royal Sea Bathing Hospital so that the treatment of their skeletal lesions could be continued.

Naturally it was necessary for these patients to have expert supervision. Dr Ray Andrews was appointed as Tuberculosis Medical Officer in Thanet in 1952, a description that was soon changed to that of Chest Physician. Originally he had no personal beds at the Royal Sea Bathing Hospital but treated the patients who were under the surgical members of the staff. Any patients of his in Thanet with pulmonary tuberculosis needing in-patient treatment had to be sent to distant sanatoria, such as Ashford, Lenham, Preston Hall, Dartford or Grove Park. Only later did some beds for pulmonary disease become available at the Royal Sea Bathing Hospital.

Dr Armstrong retired in 1954 and was succeeded by Dr Piotr Szmowski who was not designated Medical Superintendent but Executive Medical Officer. In fact, he hardly undertook any executive or administrative duties and the same essentially applied to Mr Wright who, it will be remembered, was appointed in part for administrative duties (chapter 11). By now, such activities had passed to the hands of laymen, so taking this part of the work off the shoulders of the medical men who, all the same, were continuously involved in medical administration.

A sideways glance might here be taken at this aspect of the activities of the medical staff of the hospital. All were members of the Hospital Medical Staff Committee, some of the Margate Hospital Medical Staff Committee and some of the Group Medical Committee. Indeed, some were on the Medical Staff and Group Medical Committees of Canterbury also, thus being involved in five Committees a month. As these Committees met at 8 or 8.30 p.m. and usually lasted two to three hours, it will be seen that this constituted a perceptible incursion into their private lives and was, in addition, a purely honorary commitment.

To revert to the consideration of the treatment of pulmonary tuberculosis: Dr Szmowski's background was in the treatment of this condition and he and Dr Andrews supervised this work in the hospital. It was also in 1954 that Dr Spencer Jones was appointed in parallel with Dr Andrews and the two entered fully into the great drive against tuberculosis that was current in Britain. But in the "Third World" the disease was rife and, in 1956, Dr Andrews was seconded to work in Madras under the aegis of the Medical Research Council and the World Health Organisation. His task was to study the treatment of tuberculosis under the much less favourable conditions that prevailed in India where there were no hospital facilities. His studies in the treatment of patients as out-patients with the new anti-tuberculous drugs were a complement to those being made in this country. While he was away, some of his duties were undertaken by Dr Roberts of Ashford.

However, he happily returned to Margate in 1959 to the completely new approach to the treatment of tuberculosis which he had had a hand in developing. He and Dr Spencer Jones now entered fully into the task of conducting Mass Radiography with their own Odelca Machine and of contact tracing so as to limit the spread of the disease. They supervised this work for the whole of Thanet from the Chest Clinic which they had established in Hodgson Block of the Royal Sea Bathing Hospital. So effective was the anti-tuberculous campaign nationally that patients were no longer subject to such operations for collapsing the lungs as pneumo-peritoneum, artificial pneumothorax, phrenic avulsion or crushing and multiple-stage thoracoplasty under local anaesthetic. Now, refined prescription of the new anti-tuberculous drugs allowed increasing numbers of patients to be treated in their own homes.

In the late 1950s and early 1960s there was a severe epidemic of influenza and the Chest Physicians admitted many cases to the Royal Sea Bathing Hospital to relieve the pressure on the General Hospital, including some cases with respiratory failure.

This was made possible by the success of the anti-tuberculous drugs and the other measures which had virtually eliminated tuberculosis from Britain. In the same way that orthopaedic and genito-urinary surgeons were now treating non-tuberculous conditions which came within their sphere, so the chest physicians were now able to treat similar diseases. In consequence, cases of pneumonia, chronic bronchitis, cancer of the lung, certain asbestos-induced diseases and asthma were also admitted to the Royal Sea Bathing Hospital. The advent of the steroids and broncho-dilators improved the control of asthma, another condition which was not supposed to do well in Thanet.

So it will be seen that the Department of Chest Diseases had a considerable part to play in the history of the hospital in the 1970s and 1980s. From 1974 to 1986 there were as many as 1,116 out-patient attendances and up to 373 in-patient discharges and deaths. However, with the transfer of more beds to the General Hospital, finally culminating in complete relocation of the in-patient chest work in 1984, the figures fell to around 706 and 72 respectively. So effective had been the treatment of tuberculosis in the previous three decades that it was now very rare to find a relapse of a tuberculous infection.

The Department of Diseases of the Chest made and continues to make important contributions to national studies of chest diseases and pulmonary tuberculosis which are co-ordinated by the Tuberculosis and Chest Diseases Research Unit of the Medical Research Council and the British Thoracic Association.

Both Dr Andrews and Dr Spencer Jones have retired and the work is now under the supervision of Dr A. Morgan.

One of the later and tragic complications of tuberculous bone and joint infections was involvement of the kidneys. This might even develop as late as ten years after the bone or joint lesions were fully quiescent, although it could appear sooner.

In consequence, there has always been the need for an expert in diseases of the kidneys to be available to advise where necessary. The first surgeon to fill this need was Edgar Freshman, Esq., FRCS, who was based in Canterbury but who attended the Royal Sea Bathing Hospital from early in his career in East Kent. He came to Canterbury in 1937 and, although established in General Practice originally, soon continued his surgical work at the Kent & Canterbury Hospital and at the Royal Sea Bathing Hospital. He had always had the subject of urology in the forefront of his interests and had been First Assistant to Sir Hugh Lett, urologist and President of the Royal College of Surgeons, as has already been mentioned.

During the 1939-1945 war he used to visit the Royal Sea Bathing Hospital from Canterbury from time to time, when the patients were away at Bracknell, to treat war casualties under the aegis of the EMS. He was assisted by Dr J.P. Saville Peck, who was a General Practitioner in Canterbury but also a very able anaesthetist and was also on the staff of the Kent & Canterbury Hospital. They formed, indeed, a "mobile surgical unit" which performed a very valuable service in these difficult circumstances.

Edgar Freshman, Esq., FRCS.

In the early post-war period Mr Freshman had forty beds for treatment of patients with tuberculous renal infection at the Royal Sea Bathing Hospital. His reputation in the treatment of renal tuberculosis was nation wide and he was referred patients from all over South-East England and from all the London Teaching Hospitals. He also developed very much more conservative forms of operative treatment for renal disease, such as partial nephrectomy instead of removing the whole kidney, and for ureteric strictures and bladder enlargements.

As tuberculous renal disease fell away under the influence of the anti-tuberculous drugs and environmental factors, his department developed in the same way as the Orthopaedic and Chest Diseases Departments and started to accept patients with other types of renal disease. In this way, the department flourished and remained a very busy one until his retirement in 1964. He lived for another 24 years.

Mr Freshman was replaced by Mr Martin Claridge and he developed further the treatment of non-tuberculous diseases of the urinary tract and, as the work increased in East Kent generally, he was joined by a second urologist, Mr Robert Carruthers, in 1972. While they both carry on outpatient clinics at the Royal Sea Bathing Hospital, the in-patient treatment is now in the hands of Mr Carruthers and Mr Murray.

What is of interest is that, in these clinics, there are still one or two cases of renal tuberculosis being followed up year after year. It has always been a tenet of the treatment of tuberculosis that the patients should be kept under observation, even if only annually or perhaps at five year intervals, for the rest of their lives. Not only does this allow the efficacy of treatment to be properly assessed but it allows the least suggestion of recurrence to be picked up as early as possible and necessary treatment initiated. Fortunately today, such relapses are remarkably rare.

The ultimate pattern of the treatment of surgical problems connected with the urinary system is that they will be handled at the General Hospital in Margate as the essential and highly sophisticated and expensive equipment will be installed there.

With the decreasing number of patients in the hospital being treated for tuberculosis, accommodation became available for patients suffering from rheumatoid arthritis. Princess Mary's Rehabilitation Hospital in Cliftonville had housed the rheumatology work and had been the headquarters of Physical Medicine in Thanet for many years. It was closed in 1980 and a Department opened at the Royal Sea Bathing Hospital in Maud Ward where twenty-six beds were allotted for this specialty. The broad spectrum of Physical Medicine was now housed under one roof which was a much more satisfactory arrangement.

The subject is very closely associated with orthopaedics for two reasons. Firstly, rheumatoid arthritis is such a deforming disease that orthopaedic correction and reconstruction often become necessary. Secondly, a major part of orthopaedic treatment involves rehabilitation following orthopaedic operations and this now comes under the supervision of the Specialists in Physical Medicine. There is also a very considerable demand on the Physical Medicine Department in the out-patient treatment of orthopaedic conditions so that there is a large out-patient element in the work of the department at the Royal Sea Bathing Hospital.

For many years, the Physiotherapy Department had been sited in Swinburne Ward but transferring it to Lettsom Ward in 1973 brought it to the very front of the hospital. Here out-patients and ambulances had immediate access to the clinic which is a great advantage for those with a gait handicap of whatever variety. As will be seen in the next chapter, a very welcome hydrotherapy pool was provided in Gourlay Ward which is contiguous with the rest of the department.

Dr Richard Barter and Dr Audrey Carey carried on the duties of Consultants in Physical Medicine until Dr Carey retired in 1982 and Dr Barter in 1986. Dr Robin Withrington and Dr Alison Leak now continue the good work.

179

Chapter 17

THE LEAGUE OF FRIENDS OF THE ROYAL SEA BATHING HOSPITAL

The League of Friends of the Royal Sea Bathing Hospital was formed to provide some of the financial support previously given by the London Committee. This Committee was wound up after handing the hospital over to the Ministry of Health on 4th July 1948.

The Friends formed a purely local group, having no connections with London, or, indeed, with Kent outside Thanet. Thus, although the hospital continued for some years to draw patients from all over the country and especially from London, the Medway towns and other parts of the South-East Thames Region, the source of voluntary funds was severely reduced. Moreover, voluntary fund-raising started from nothing, for the considerable resources available to the hospital on the "appointed day" had to be handed over in their entirety to the Government.

In spite of these severe limitations, it is not an exaggeration to say that, with the exception of the improvements to the operating theatre and to Maud and Lettsom Wards (which were essential to the setting up of the General Orthopaedic Unit), every major improvement at the hospital for the next thirty-five years was due to the Friends.

This policy was in accord with the determination expressed by Dr Fairley, who became Senior Administrative Medical Officer of the South-East Thames Metropolitan Regional Hospital Board in 1960, to spend no more money on the hospital. Dr Fairley was, in this, simply following the policy adopted by Mr Enoch Powell, then Minister of Health, to concentrate all hospital development in District General Hospitals. The outlook for all special hospitals became bleak, many of which have been closed, and from then onwards, throughout what was, in some respects, its most active period, the Royal Sea Bathing Hospital laboured under a "planning blight" which was relieved only by the League of Friends.

It was not until 1983 that the Hospital Authorities undertook any but the most meagre measures of maintenance. It was only at that time, when the operating theatre was declared unsafe for operating, for lack of proper maintenance, that they built a completely new theatre suite as there was nowhere else in which to accommodate the work of the Royal Sea Bathing Hospital.

The League has been fortunate in that, during its forty years of work, it has had only two chairmen, both of whom had the well-being of the hospital as his chief interest. The first chairman was Mr Frank Wallis, LDS, who had been Dental Surgeon to the hospital from before nationalisation and who continued in that post afterwards until his retirement in 1958. He gathered a strong committee of local residents to start the League in 1948 and remained chairman until 1969. It is an interesting illustration of the lack of co-operation between the Thanet towns at that time that the committee members were all Margate people. Ramsgate and Broadstairs residents played no part, although their interests were as important as were those of the citizens of Margate.

The principle guiding the work of the Friends was that they would undertake any work that served the interests of the patients other than matters directly affecting medical treatment, which they regarded as the duty of the Government. Fortunately for the hospital, they interpreted the principle in a very generous way for most of their major undertakings did, in fact, concern the patients' treatment. Furthermore, they regarded the well-being of doctors and nurses as coming within their remit.

One of the first undertakings of the Friends was to improve the conditions of the nurses' home, including the provision of washing machines for the nurses' use.

A much more major undertaking on behalf of the nursing staff was the collection of money to finance the building of a nurses' recreation hall, later to become known as the Wallis Memorial Hall. This project occupied the Friends for some six years until 1959, when the foundation stone was laid. The hall was large enough to seat 300 and had a stage, games room with a full-sized billiard table, kitchen and ample cloakroom accommodation. The hall was, of course, used by patients as well as nurses and not only transformed the social life of the hospital but gave an excellent venue for the meetings of the many visits of medical and para-medical organisations in the years to come.

As well as its work for the nurses, the League began, during the 1950s, the first of a number of projects to improve the comfort of patients when it installed curtains round the beds in all the adult wards. Until then, the patients had to rely, for privacy, on mobile screens. There was much discussion as to the dangers of cross-infection that might result from the new curtains, but fears proved unfounded and few single measures made more difference to the comfort of the patients at the time. Also, during the 1950s, television was becoming an accepted amenity and the League paid for the installation of sets in the adult wards. Mobile telephones were also provided throughout the hospital.

The last major work undertaken during Mr Wallis' chairmanship was the building of a new covered way between the old part of the hospital and the KG Wards and recreation hall. This also gave covered access to the new school building which was provided by the Kent County Council but equipped, in part, with a contribution from the League of Friends.

The Hydrotherapy Pool.

The metal workshop.

182

Following Mr Wallis came Mr F.J. Howland and, in 1971, under his chairmanship, the League opened an appeal for the largest of all its projects — the provision of a heated indoor hydrotherapy pool. This was to be sited in Gourlay Ward where it would be linked with the Physiotherapy Department. This had been moved to Lettsom Ward from its previous situation in Swinburne Ward next to the operating theatre. The first estimate for the pool was £13,000 but the final cost proved to be £20,000 and this sum was raised in under two years.

A vital factor in the success of this appeal was the help that the League obtained from Mr Harry Anish, who became Mayor of Margate in 1971 and who made the financing of the pool his major charity concern during his period of office. The pool was opened in 1972 but, alas, it is not filled with sea water!

Under Mr Howland the League financed or helped to finance a number of other important projects, including the re-equipping of the metal workshop of the Surgical Appliance Department in 1977-78. Later, in 1980-81, when plans were being made for the re-siting of the other sections of the Appliance Department, the League played an important part in the appeal which finally financed the improvement. These new workshops had the advantage that, being no longer sited in a basement, they were much more pleasant for the highly skilled staff to work in and also were better equipped.

In making improvements to the front hall of the hospital, the league co-operated with the Women's Royal Voluntary Service and later, in 1982-83, it provided a new telephone switchboard for the hospital at a cost of more than £3,000.

At the time of writing, Mr F.J. Howland continues as the League's chairman and under him, in spite of the uncertain future of the hospital, the League continues to play a vital part in supporting its work. As an example of this, as a result of the Area Health Authority's continuing refusal to undertake any but the most trivial of maintenance, the King George I Ward, farthest from the main hospital buildings, became so dilapidated that it had to be taken out of use and the covered way out to the school, King George II Ward and the Wallis Recreation Hall similarly degenerated. The League of Friends repaired the covered way but the ward remains uninhabitable.

It is a sad example of the difference in investment, design and workmanship that the post-1914-1918 war buildings failed to stand up to the ravages of time in the way that Lettsom's and Erasmus Wilson's buildings of the eighteenth and nineteenth centuries did!

Mention of the Women's Royal Voluntary Service brings into mind the excellent work it also does on a completely voluntary basis in providing for the needs of both patients and their visitors. While neither come from so far afield as in the old days, they still welcome the light refreshments that the Women's Royal Voluntary Service provides in a most convenient position immediately adjacent to the entrance of the hospital and the ambulance set down and pick up site.

This is another example of the still prevailing spirit of service that informs the citizens of Margate and, happily, of the country as a whole, in spite of the professed philosophy in some political persuasions that it is demeaning to receive charity!

Chapter 18
AVE ATQUE VALE

And so we come to the present time, as far as it is possible to keep up with events.

The Royal Sea Bathing Hospital remains in the forefront of orthopaedic surgery, of urology, of anaesthetics and of physical medicine. All the most modern methods are in daily use for the treatment of patients. Not every ward is in use, owing to exigencies of finance, but the work is concentrated and the turnover of patients high. From the three years that was not uncommonly the duration of treatment of patients in the first one and a half centuries of the hospital's existence, one or two weeks is the longest that the great majority of patients have to stay in nowadays and often the stay is shorter still.

Some indication of the changes that have occurred may be gathered from a comparison of the frontispiece with the illustration of the front of the hospital today.

Happily, it is possible to see the original facade in the tranquility of the central quadrangle. Modern transport differs somewhat from the old "Margate Hoy" although the fare may be a little more expensive. But, alas, the hospital may not survive for so very long. There are many reasons why this should be so and amongst them is the policy of successive Ministers in charge of the Health Services, as mentioned in the last chapter. The aim is to discontinue all special hospitals and to absorb their work into the general hospitals. This has already led to the reduction of more than twenty per cent in the bed strength of orthopaedic hospitals nationally and even as this chapter is being penned, the newspapers report that the Middlesex Hospital, which has recently absorbed the Royal National Orthopaedic Hospital, is having its orthopaedic bed strength reduced!

Apart from the administrative tidiness of having work concentrated in convenient units, it is true that medicine has become so sophisticated that it is impossible to provide every hospital with the enormously expensive equipment which seems to be necessary today. This is partly, alas, to protect, as far as possible, the Health Services and servants from the public's growing tendency to resort to litigation, which is having an extremely adverse effect on every aspect of medicine and patient care. It is hoped that such conglomerate hospitals will be fully staffed and equipped for all aspects of medicine and surgery, but this is a patent illusion. It will always be impossible to provide *every* service in every general hospital for the simple reason that neurosurgery, thoracic surgery and plastic surgery, to

The frontage today!

The original frontage seen in the tranquillity of the Quadrangle. Drawing specially done for the History of the Royal Sea Bathing Hospital by Robert Carruthers, Esq., FRCS, Consultant Urologist to the Royal Sea Bathing Hospital, December 1989.

Modern transport. A change from the Margate Hoy!

name a few, demand a huge population to support their departments and will never have units in every general hospital.

Another disadvantage that particularly affects orthopaedics is that, once an orthopaedic department is situated in a general hospital, there is virtually no way in which the beds can be reserved for orthopaedics, every other surgical department and mounting trauma overflow into them and they cannot be maintained for orthopaedic patients from the waiting lists.

A further disadvantage is that it is unlikely that orthopaedic units in general hospitals will have their own operating theatres for many years to come. Sharing theatres with other surgical disciplines inevitably increases the risk of wound infection and this is far more serious when bones and joints become infected than in other tissues of the body.

It would have been nice to think that orthopaedic hospitals could have been regionally funded and have regional catchment areas, when the small number of such hospitals could be regarded in the same way as neurosurgical, thoracic and plastic units and could be built up to the necessary standards. This would retain the expertise that they have generated over the years in all grades of staff and make the practice of orthopaedics as efficient as it could possibly be and maintain the teaching opportunities which are the envy of the world and continuously draw graduates from all over the world to further their orthopaedic training.

If District planning could contemplate a Royal Sea Bathing Hospital without the King George Wards and most of the main lawn but with the remainder of the hospital being updated, even including the provision of a second operating theatre, its future development might be considerably less costly than at present envisaged and might leave the Royal Sea Bathing Hospital to carry on its valuable contribution to orthopaedics, urology and rheumatology in Kent unhindered. With the possible installation of a lift and extension of "New" Ward over Maud, the bed strength could easily reach 150, including the beds on the fully enclosed balconies. Such a unit should be quite large enough to attract both nursing and resident medical staff and obtain the approval of the Royal Colleges.

Another possible reason for the impending demise of the Royal Sea Bathing Hospital is that its site is one of enormous commercial value of which the Health Service Administration cannot possibly fail to take advantage. However, if the KG Wards and the equivalent space in front of them were sold, as suggested in the previous paragraph, it might well pay for the development outlined there without any call on National Health Service funds whatsoever!

Unfortunately, this seems to be no more than a pipe-dream and orthopaedics will continue to suffer drastic reduction in beds and facilities and yet have the approbrium of "doing nothing" about its rapidly expanding waiting lists.

It is hoped, in any case, that the buildings of Lettsom and Erasmus Wilson may survive as they are "Listed Buildings" and represent important architectural features of their periods.

In addition, it is impossible to contemplate the destruction of the chapel and it is encouraging to learn that there may be certain religious organisations interested in it. It is certainly far too fine to be allowed to succumb to the developers' bulldozer!

And so this history ends on a rather sad note and bids "Ave atque Vale" to the Royal Sea Bathing Hospital.

At least, the Royal Sea Bathing Hospital has made superb provision for the "scrofulous poor" for two hundred years, for their accommodation in the best possible surroundings and their treatment in the best manner known to science at the time. Whether they were the victims of bone and joint tuberculosis or of glands, kidneys, or other viscera infected with the tubercle bacillus, or more recently of other orthopaedic, urological or chest diseases, the Royal Sea Bathing Hospital has given them the best chance they could have had of looking forward to a life free, as far as humanly possible, from the complications of their dread diseases.

But in the provision of such a service there is a price to be paid. In a hospital for the treatment of tuberculosis, particularly in the days when the cause of the disease and the proper protection against infection were not or not properly known, many of the staff must have contracted tuberculosis as

Mr Evernden (l.c.) says in his letter. Some of these will almost certainly have succumbed.

Amongst those who died after only a very short period of service or at an unusually early age while still in the service of the hospital and who, therefore, may have been victims of tuberculosis caught in the course of their duties are the following:

Dr Eyles, 1812.
George Horatio Chestfield, Superintendent for twenty-five years but aged only fifty-five at his death in harness in 1896.
Nurse Fanny Matilda Pell, 1902.
Dr C.L. Claud Owen, 1903, aged twenty-three.
Dr Harnett, after less than a year as Visiting Surgeon, 1905.
Nurse Christina Lawrence, 1908.
And two nurses who died nursing patients in the cholera epidemic of 1849.
There may well be many more who remain unsung except anonymously.

To all such, as well as to all who have worked over the years for the patients to the best of their ability, and to all who have contributed to its support without which it could not have existed, full tribute is due.

In spite of all the adverse factors that continuously assail the Royal Sea Bathing Hospital from every side, the uncertainty of its future existence, the uncertainty of maintaining sufficient staff, the uncertainty of funding and the uncertainty of its physical maintenance, the morale of both patients and staff remains as high as it has ever been.

Whatever its future, THE ROYAL SEA BATHING HOSPITAL can hold its head high and feel that, for TWO HUNDRED YEARS, it has fully implemented the farsighted vision of its founder. JOHN COAKLEY LETTSOM.

As we go to press, it has been stated that the closure of the Royal Sea Bathing Hospital will not now take place "in the foreseeable future".

Mr P.F. Wright   Mr T. Glyn Thomas   Mr D.J. Klugman

Mr M.E. Conybeare   Mr I.B.M. Stephen   Mr N. Blackburn

Mr Martin Claridge   Dr Kulasinghe   Dr Peter Read

190

Appendix 1
Present and Retired Staff

Present Staff at the time of going to press.

Orthopaedic Surgeons
D.J. Klugman
M.E. Conybeare
I.B.M. Stephen
N. Blackburn

Urological Surgeons
R. Carruthers
K. Murray

Rheumatologists
Dr R.H. Withrington
Dr A.M. Leak

Chest Physician
Dr A. Morgan

G-U. Physician
Dr R.P. Sarkhel

Paediatricians
Dr J. Appleyard
Dr D.M. Cook

Anaesthetists
Dr A. Ferguson
Dr N. Kulasinghe
Dr K. Lewin
Dr M. Mikhael
Dr K. Proctor

Radiologist
Dr R.F. Cant

Nursing Staff
Senior Nurse Manager,
Mrs Y. Brown (Matron)

Night Sisters
Mrs Grigg
Mrs Tamplin
Mrs Turner

Ward Sisters
L. Crosara
J. Radford
F. Richardson

Ward Charge Nurse
J. De Souza
T. O'Connor

Theatres and Recovery
Sisters A. Carrington,
S. Bowskill,
H. Torres-Tigas,
Charge Nurse P. Farmer

191

Dr Ann Ferguson

Dr D.M. Cook

Dr R.H. Withrington

Mrs Y.D. Brown

Sir John Cadell, KBE

Dr M.M. Voysey

Dr R.H. Andrews

Dr R.F. Cant

192

Administrative, Ancillary and Supporting Staff
District General Manager. Vice-Admiral Sir John Cadell, KBE (R.N.Retd.).
Unit General Manager. Dr M.M. Voysey.
Superintendent Radiographer. D. Richardson.
Superintendent Physiotherapist. Miss L. Nicholl.
Orthotist Manager. W. Knight.
Senior Occupational Therapist. Mrs L. Keefe.
General Administrative Assistant. Mrs V.M. Chapman.
Medical Records Office Manager. Miss A. Norris.
Assistant Catering Manager. Miss D. Belsey.
Domestic Supervisor. Mrs. B. Paskell.
Assistant Head Porter. E. Brownlee.
Accommodation Officer. Mrs A. Shutler.
Residence Manager. Miss A. Webb.

Chairman of the League of Friends
Mr F.J. Howland

Retired Consultants

Dr R.H. Andrews
Dr R. Barter
Dr A. Carey
Mr M. Claridge
Dr J. Forsaith

Dr R. Kirkpatrick
Dr N.P. Read
Dr Spencer-Jones
Mr F.G. St Clair Strange
Mr P.R. Wright

Retired Nursing Staff

Mr Austin
Mrs Call
Miss Collier
Miss D'Arcy
Miss Dawson
Mrs Evans
Mrs Francis
Miss Haly
Miss Kingfisher
Mrs Mack

Mrs Neave
Miss Needham
Mrs Notcutt
Mrs Peall
Mrs Stevens, J.P.
Miss Stidwell
Mr Stockbridge
Mrs Wilbourne
Miss Wilson

Retired Non-Medical Staff

Mr Belcher
Mr Burdett
Mr Christian
Mr Pickwick

Appendix 2

WORDING OF MEMORIAL PLAQUES IN THE CHAPEL

Armstrong, Basil. (marble relief)
Basil William Armstrong, OBE, MC, MB, BS, MRCS, LRCP. Born 12th July 1889. Died 14th May 1958. Medical Superintendent of the Royal Sea Bathing Hospital 1923-1954.

Bangham, A.W.
A plaque erected to the memory of A.W. Bangham, aged 56. For 39 years organist to the hospital. Died 10th July 1937.

Chestfield, George H.
In affectionate remembrance of George Horatio Chestfield who for 35 years was superintendent of this Hospital. He died at St Peters, Thanet, on the 27th of June 1896, aged 55 years. "There remains a rest for the people of God".

Heathcote, Francis.
In memory of Francis Heathcote, Benefactor of this Hospital. Died 19th March 1899. This plaque was erected in 1900.

Hilberry, Miss L.
In memory of Louise Illington (née Hilberry) Matron of this Hospital from September 1887 to August 1895. Died February 24th 1929.

Lennard, Sir Henry Farnaby, Bt. (statuette: St George and the dragon)
Henry Farnaby Lennard, Bt. Amicus certus.

Lawrence, Nurse Christina H.
In memory of Nurse Christina H. Lawrence who died in the service of the Hospital. 17th May 1908.

Lettsom, John Coakley.
In memory of that true and zealous philanthropist, John Coakley Lettsom, MD, FRS, &c. &c. a member of the Society of Friends who amongst his many acts of practical benevolence Founded this Infirmary July 2nd 1791. Born 1744. Died 1815.

Monahan, Olive.
In memory of Olive Monahan. Assistant Matron of this Hospital 1946 to 1966. Hon. Archivist. 1966 to 1975. Died 5th November 1975.

Owen, C.L. Claude.
In memory of C.L. Claude Owen, MRCS Eng. LPCD Lond. who died whilst in office as Junior Resident Surgeon to this Hospital. 16th January 1903. Aged 23 years.

Pell, Nurse Fanny M.
In memory of Nurse Fanny Matilda Pell, who died in the service of the Hospital. 13th June 1902.

Wilson, Dame Charlotte M.
This organ was presented to the Hospital in memory of Dame Charlotte Mary, widow of Sir Erasmus Wilson.

Wilson, Sir Erasmus.
The Chapel, the New Wing and other additions and Improvements to this Infirmary were bestowed on the Institution AD 1882 by Sir Erasmus Wilson, MD, FRS, Fellow and President of the Royal College of Surgeons of England. This tablet is erected by the Directors and Governors of this Institution as a record of this munificent gift so generously intended to relieve the sufferings and promote the cure of the scrofulous poor of Great Britain. John Creaton, Lt. Col. Chairman.

Appendix 3
ERASMUS WILSON'S STIMULATING
HAIR WASH/DRESSING
(Courtesy of Mrs Schuster)

Ol. Santal. Flav.	3 minims
Ol. Bergamotte.	2½ drachms.
Ol. Carophyllic.	10 minims.
Ol. Lavand.	40 minims.
Aq. Rosae Trip.	10 fl. ozs.
Industrial Spirit	48 fl. ozs.
Aq. Dest.	20 fl. ozs.
Tinct. Capsici.	40 minims.
Ext. Quassiae.	½ fl. drachm.
Di-ethyl phthalate.	6½ fl. drachms.

This was made up until 1971 by D.L. Lewis, Ltd., Chemists in Ealing. It makes four pints, half a gallon! Some shampoo! But perhaps this was a hairdresser's stock.

Erasmus Wilson got some disapproval from his colleagues for this. But, after all, he was a Dermatologist!

Appendix 4
CALOT'S PASTES

No. 1

Phenol Camphor.	6 gms.
Napththol Camphor.	6 gms.
Guiacol.	8 gms.
Iodoform.	20 gms.
Lanoline.	100 gms.

Melts at 104 degrees F

No. 2

The same but with only half the amount of Phenol and Napththol Camphor and of Iodoform. It has the same melting point.

Calot's fluid was presumably a similar prescription but, perhaps, without the lanoline but some other more fluid vehicle. I remember using it at Lowestoft and it was a liquid and did not have to be melted. It was used to infuse tuberculous abscesses and was said to break down the fibrin which used to make aspiration so difficult. I do not remember that it made very much difference!

References

C & T DHA stands for Canterbury & Thanet District Health Authority Archives.
KCC stands for Kent County Council Archives.
RSBHA stands for Royal Sea Bathing Hospital Archives.
RSBHUA stands for Royal Sea Bathing Hospital uncatalogued archives.

Abraham, J.J.	1933	Lettsom, His Life and Times, Friends and Descendants. London, Wm. Heinemann Medical Books.
Admissions Book	1821-27	RSBHA 17.
Albee, F.H.	1915	Bone Graft Surgery. Philadelphia, W.B. Saunders.
"An Invalid"	1855	"Margate in Winter". Daily Telegraph, 2nd April.
Ashcroft, Eileen	1939	Daily Mirror, 9th Feb.
Ball & Evans	1932	Diseases of the Kidney. London, J. & A. Churchill.
Bick, E.M.	1948	Source Book of Orthopaedics. Baltimore, the Williams & Wilkins Co. 69-70.
Bill for Dinner	1800	RSBHA 64-66.
Bread for Poultices	1800	ibid 67-69.
Brockman, M.	1800	Bill for Bathing Patients. ibid 72-74.
C & T DHA	1872-1964	Docs. 1(72), 4(81), 6(1900), 7(04), 8 & 16(19), 11(26), 22(64).
Cazin, H.	1885	*De L'Influence des Bains de Mer sur la Scrofule des Enfants. (Prix Capuron. 1883), par le Dr H. Cazin Médicin-Chirurgien de l'Hôpital maritime de Berck-sur-Mer et de l'Hôpital Nathaniel Rothschild. Lauréat de l'Academie de Médicine, Chevalier de la Légion d'Honneur Paris, etc, etc.*
Chalk, W.O.	1837	RSBHA 50.
Charnley, John	1961	Arthroplasty of the Hip by a Low-Friction Technique. J. Bone & Jt. Surg. 43-B. 601.
Cobb	1823	RSBHA 48.
Cobb, P.	1947	ibid. 49.
Cobb, W.F.	1836	Memoir of the late Francis Cobb, Esq., of Margate, compiled from his journals and letters. Maidstone, 43 & 53.
Connor, P.	1978	Sunday Times Colour Supt. Sept. 10.
Cope, Z.	1959	History of the Royal College of Surgeons of England. London, Anthony Blond. 61.
Courts of Directors, Minutes, KCC all MH/T1	1791	A1.
	1822	A7.
	1826-51	Quoted by Whyman, q.v. 16.7.1828. 8.11.1828. 9.4.1834. 8.5.1851.
	1851-98	A1 of 1852, A5 of 1851, 1853, A7 of 1874. A8 of 1862, 1874, 1885, 1886, 1887. R1 of 1851.
de Kruif, P.	1933	Men Against Death. London, Jonathan Cape.
Directors' Minute Book	1871-76	RSBHA 15.

Dover Express & Intelligencer	1851	Quoted by Whyman, q.v.
"	1859	ibid. 9th July.
Evernden, S.	1986	RSBHA 401.
Executive Minute Book	1871-79	ibid 11.
Field, A.G.	1852	KCC MH/T1 A1.
Five Shilling List	1858	RSBHA 9.
Foyle, C.	1989	Personal Communication.
Francis, H.	1989	Personal Communication.
General Sea Bathing Infirmary, Minutes	1811-37	KCC MH/T1 Ramsgate Library. 30.8.1813. 19-20.
Gentleman's Magazine	1896-97	LXVI 608-9.
"	1896-97	LXVII 841.
Gibbs, D.D.	1989	Personal Communication. RSBHUA.
Gilbert, E.M.	1975	Brighton, Old Ocean's Bauble, Hassocks. Flare Books, John Spiers. 12,14.
Gray, Thomas	1766	Quoted by Hillier, q.v.
Hadley, R.M.	1959	Life and Works of Sir William James Erasmus Wilson 1808-1884. Med. Hist. 1959.3.159. 215-247.
Henley, W.E.	1926	Poems. London, Macmillan & Co.
"	1949	"Invictus" Oxford Book of English Verse. Ed. Quiller-Couch. Oxford, The Clarendon Press.
Heyerdahl, T.	1958	Aku Aku. London, Unwin Hyman.
Hibbs, R.A.	1926	A Preliminary Report of 20 Cases of Hip Joint Tuberculosis treated by an Operation devised to eliminate Motion by Fusing the Joint. J. Bone & Jt. Surg. 8.522.
Hillier, Caroline	1982	The Bulwark Shore, "Thanet and the Cinque Ports". London, Eyre Methuen, 1980, Paladin Books, 1982, 73, 74, 295.
House-Keeping Book	1820-37	RSBHA 358.
Howard, P.	1978	The Needle starts a new Century. Times, 14th Sept.
HRH Prince Regent	1812	RSBHA 3.
Hugli, J. & Nicod, L.	1975	*Centieme Anniversaire de l'Hôpital Orthopédique de la Suisse Romande. Les Presses Centrales de Lausanne.*
Iken, Mrs	1823	RSBHA 48.
Illustrated London News	1887	Sep.11th, p.298. RSBHA 388.
Isle of Thanet Gazette	1926	Sep. 25th.
"	1946	July 26th.
Jerrold, W.	1907	Highways and Byways in Kent. London, McMillan & Co. 109, 111.
Journal of an Excursion to Ramsgate	1829	Quoted by Whyman, q.v.
Judet, J., Judet, R., LaGrange, J., Dunoyer, J.	1954	Resection-Reconstruction of the Hip. Tr. Nissen, K.I. Edinburgh & London, E.S. Livingstone Ltd.
Key, L.A.	1936	Urinary Tract Complications in the prolonged Immobilisation of Children. Brit. Med. J. June 6th. 1150.
King, T.	1934	Recent Intracapsular Fractures of the Neck of the Femur. A critical Consideration of the Treatment & a Description of a new Technique. Med. J. of Australia. Jan. 6th. p.5.
Lamb, C.	1833	Essays of Elia. "The Old Margate Hoy". Reprinted 1908. London, J.M. Dent & Co. 207-211.

Lettsom, J.C.	1788	Anniversary Oration to the Medical Society of London. History of the Origin of Medicine. London, E.C. Dilly. RSBHA 1.
,,	1801	Hints Designed to Promote Beneficence, Temperance and Medical Science. III 6, 235-237, 148.
,,	1804	RSBHA 2.
Lewis, H.	1786	"An Excursion to Margate in the month of June, 1786". Quoted by Whyman, q.v.
Licensed Victuallers' Gazette & Hotel Courier	1875	Messrs Cobb & Co.'s Brewery at Margate. 4th Dec. 395-396.
Lister, J.	1867	On a new Method of Treating Compound Fractures, Abscesses, etc. Lancet, I. 326, 357, 387, 507.
London Chronicle	1792	RSBHA 47. 28th-30th June. p.622.
McLellan, D.	1973	Karl Marx. His Life & Thought. London, Macmillan & Co.
McKee, G.K.	1951	Artificial Hip Joint. J. Bone & Jt. Surg. 33-B. 465.
McMurray, T.P.	1935	Osteo-arthritis of the Hip Joint. Brit. J. Surg. 22.716.
Madden, P.	1989	"Just Like That". Channel 4 T.V. 28th December.
Marsden, C.	1947	The English at the Seaside. London, Collins. Quoted by Hillier, q.v.
Matthews, J.	1836	RSBHA 41-43.
,,	1837	ibid 45, 369, 370.
,,	1840	ibid 368.
,,	1841	ibid 367.
Minutes	1791-93	Original Minutes of the General Sea Bathing Infirmary. MS held in Kent County Council's Archives at Ramsgate Library. 2 & 11.7. of 1791 & 15.6.1792.
Morris, E.W.	1910	A History of the London Hospital. London, Edward Arnold.
Newman, H.	1969	North-East & East Kent. London, Penguin Books.
New Margate, Ramsgate & Broadstairs Guide	1797	Reviewed in the Gentlemen's Magazine. LVXII. 841.
,,	1816	6th Edition. Margate. 100.
Paget, J.	1876-77	Med. Chir. Trans. London, 60, 37.
Pettigrew, T.J.	1817	The Memoirs of the Life and Writings of the late John Coakley Lettsom, MD, LL.D, FRS, with a Selection from his Correspondence. 3 Vols. London, Longman, Hurst, Rees, Orme & Brown. I.117-8.
Picture of Margate	1840	RSBHA 56.
,,	1845	Oulton.
Portrait of the Rev. Hodgson	1856	RSBHA 19.
P.R.O. 107/468/6	1841	Quoted by Whyman, q.v.
Provisions Book	1820-37	RSBHA 359.
Quinquenial Governors	1902	RSBHA 160 p.67.
Raistrick, A.	1950	Quakers in Science and Industry. 311.
Register of Patients	1801-16	RSBHA 346.
Reports of the Court of Directors	1851	Quoted by Whyman. q.v.
,,	1901	RSBHA 160-61.
,,	1918	RSBHA 181.

Reprints:
Armstrong, B. 1947 Tuberculous Adenitis. RSBHA 292.
" 1953 Abdominal Tuberculosis. RSBHA 293-95.
" & Jarman, T.F. 1936 Saucerization and Skin Grafting for Chronic Osteo-
myelitis. RSBHA 291.
Resident Surgeon's
Reports 1872-89 KRO.MH/T1.M2.1. Quoted by Whyman, q.v.
Royal Sea Bathing
Hospital Reports 1936-41 Report of 1938. p.7.
Rules and Regulations 1911 RHBSA 218-219.
Russell, R. 1750 *De Tabe Glandulari sive de Aquae Marinae in Morbis
Glandularum Dissertatio.* Oxford, Jacob Fletcher and
London, J. Rivington.
" 1753 A Dissertation concerning the use of Sea Water in
Diseases of Glands. Oxford.
Seddon, H.J. & Strange,
F.G.St.C. 1940 Sacro-Iliac Tuberculosis. Brit. J. Surgery. 28.193.
Steward's Bill 1800 RSBHA 63.
Strange, F.G.St.C. 1960 "New Inventions". Plaster Turning Frame. Lancet 1.
No.7115. p.96.
" 1963 The Prognosis in Sacro-Iliac Tuberculosis. Brit. J.
Surg. 50.561.
" 1965 "The Hip". London, William Heinemann Medical.
Syrus (Attributed) 1st Cent. Proverbial.
Thomas, T.G. 1973 The Character of Erasmus Wilson. Med. Soc. London.
Transactions. LXXXIX 1973. 288-291.
Visitors' Book 1867-1935 RSBHA 14.
Walker, J.T. 1875 RSBHUA.
Whyman, J. 1975 MS Ph.D. Thesis. An Important Chapter in English
Medical & Social History. The Royal Sea Bathing
Hospital at Margate. University of Kent at Canter-
bury. RSBHA 366.
Wilson, J.C. 1927 Extra-Articular Fusion of the Tuberculous Hip Joint.
California & West Medical J. 27, 744.
Wright, P.R. 1965 In "The Hip". F.G. St. Clair Strange. London, Heine-
mann Medical. pp.216, 217.

202

INDEX OF NAMES

The following do not appear in the index as they occur so often that the string of numbers would be meaningless:

Armstrong, Lettsom, Wilson, Board/Court of Governors, Margate, Matron.

Brousdorph, Erasmus – 75
Brown, John – 149
Brown, Dr R.W. – 43
Brown, Dr Thomas – 46
Brown, Mrs Yvonne, Matron – 174
Bryer, Dr – 164,165
Burdett, Mr – 159
Burnett, J. Leger – 88 ·
Burrows, H. Jackson – 156
Burton, Lady – 46
Butler, R. Weedon – 28,159,161
Butler, Rev. Weedon – 27,28,159

Cadell, Sir John – 94
Cambridge, the Duke of – 94
Campbell, Major-Gen. F.L. – 95
Canham, Dr – 66
Cant, Dr Ronald – 148
Canterbury, the Archbishop of –
   see Archbishop of
Carey, Dr Audrey – 179
Carlton, Mary Ann – 91
Carmichael, Sister – 164,165
Carroll, Lewis – 131
Carruthers, Robert – 178,186
Carson, Rt. Hon. Lady – 133
Carter, F.C. – 84
Carter, Capt. Henry – 75
Cassell, Sir Ernest – 108
Cauchoix, Dr Jean – 162,163
Cayly, Dr W. – 95
Cazin, Dr – 84,85,175
Chalk, Emily – 63
Chalk, Dr William Oliver – 51,59,61,63,104
Charnley, Sir John – 167
Cheadle, Dr W.B. – 95
Chestfield, G.H. – 73,189,194
Christ, Miracles of – 81 & Col. Suppt.
Christian, Fred – 118,119,123,141
Churchill, Rev. W.H. – 123
Claridge, Martin – 178
Clarke, H.C. – 111
Cleveland, Mr – 113
Clifton, Viscount – 94
Coakley, Mary – 13
Coates, Dr – 164,165
Cobb, Dr – 47,54,71
Cobb, Dr A.B. – 95
Cobb, Francis – 47
Cobb, Francis – 27,46,47,147
Cobb, Francis William – 46,47
Cobb, Mrs Phyllis – 55,71,92
Cocks, E.L.S. – 90

Coleridge, Samuel Taylor – 47
Collier, Miss, Matron – 86
Collis, Thomas – 50,51
Collot d'Herbois – 33
Colvin, Dr H.J.A. – 136
Combe, C. – 18
Conybeare, Martin – 169,173
Cook, Anne – 46
Cooper, Lady Agnes – 83
Cooper, Tommy – 170
Cope, Rev. A.D. – 95
Cornford, F.J. – 129,133
Cottrell, Dr – 163
Coullie, Dr – 101
Coursou, Dr – 163
Cozens, Zachariah – 37,39,49,73
Crameri, Dr P.V. – 118
Crenshaw, Dr & Mrs A. – 164,165
Crewe, Sir J.H. – 69
Croft, John – 90,95
Curling, H. – 84
Curtiss, James – 168

D'Arcy, Sister – 132,135
D'Arcy Power, Sir – 86,104,106,111
d'Herbois, Collot — see Collot d'Herbois
Dall, Prof. George – 172
Daniel, W. Neave – 37
Davies, F.W.T. – 172
Dawkes, Nurse E. Florence – 103
Dawson of Penn, Lord – 123
de Rothschild, Baron – 97
Derby, Earl of – 94,98
Dickinson, W. Howship – 90,95
Dickson, Dr – 111,159,161
Dickson, J. – 111,113,159,161
Dixon, J. – 75
Dixon, W.E. – 70
Dodgson, Dr Harry – 93
Doughty, Miss – 109; see Howland
Dover, Bishop of – 133
Down Bros – 87
Du Pan, C. – 34
Du Pan, E.M. – 34
Duckworth, Sir Dyce – 90,95
Duncan, Dr – 101,120
Dunn, Sir Thomas – 87
Dunoyer, Dr – 167
Duriez, Dr – 163

East, Miss Phyllis – 109
Easton, P.A. – 90
Easton, P.S. – 87

204

Edlmann, Mrs C.E. – 92,93,119
Edlmann, Mrs E. – 92
Edlmann, Mrs J. – 47
Edlmann, Mrs J.L. – 92
Egerton, Hon. Thomas – 95
Elisha – 80,81
Elliott, Major – 95
Ells, Geoffrey – 114
Elyard, Col. Evans – 87
Eve, Sir Frederick – 104
Evernden, Stanley – 120,121,189
Eyles, Dr – 43,189

Fairley, Dr J.S.S. – 146,180
Faraboeuf – 89
Farquhar, Sir Walter – 37
Ferguson, Dr Ann – 159
Ferrier, Dr David – 95
Field, A.G. – 65
Fields, Gracie – 120
Finnie, Mrs Hannah – 102
Forbes, J. – 27
Ford, E. – 18
Forester, Lord – 87,95
Forsaith, Dr J. – 148
Forsyth, Mrs – 46
Foster, Mrs Mary, Matron – 49
Foyle, Christina – 121,123
Frampton, Dr Algernon – 37
Francis, Mrs Hilda, Matron –
    129,130,133,145,156
Freeman, Charles – 88
Freshman, Edgar – 123,145,177,178
Frome, E. – 46
Frome, S. – 37
Fryer, E. – 46
Furse, J. – 59

Galloway, Sir J. – 104
Gardiner, Mrs – 89
Garrow, Rev. David – 46
Garrow, Sir William – 46
Garthshore, Dr Maxwell – 37
Gass, D. – 40,41
Gauvain, Sir Henry – 136
Gehazi – 81
George, Edna – 126
Gibbs, Alan – 90
Gibbs, Michael – 46
Gilbert, Rose – 96
Gillett, Nurse – 97
Gillison, Dr Mrs – 90
Gimson, Dr Thomas – 73
Girdlestone, Gaythorne – 136

Glockner, Dr & Mrs – 164,165
Godlee, Sir Rickman – 95
Gosse, J. Hope – 133
Gould, A. Pearce – 95
Gray, Commander – 94,95
Gray, Sir A.H.M. & Lady – 133
Gray, Thomas – 29
Green, Alan – 173
Green, Gavin – 172,174
Green, Olivier – 66
Green, Dr T.H. – 95
Gresham, Dr H. – 92
Grey, Dr Thomas – 46
Grimthorpe, Lord – 94
Groves, Archdeacon Henry O. – 106,109
Guthrie, G.V. – 66

Hague, Dr – 164,165
Haighton, J. – 18
Halford, Henry – 66
Hall, Dr, Miss E.M. – 107
Hall, Dr Edmund M. – 92
Hallett (child) – 61
Halsbury, Earl of – 94
Halsult, Mr & Mrs – 69
Hannay, Mrs, Matron – 94,95,97,105
Harcourt, Miss Hilda, Matron – see Francis
Hardman, Nurse – 111
Hardman, Sister – 133
Hardy, Mrs – 147,148
Hardy, Charles S. – 94
Harkness, Miss Janet A.E. – 124
Harman, Mr – 55
Harnett, Dr C.J. – 92,95,101
Harrison, B. Guy – 133
Hatfeild, Capt. & Mrs – 99,133
Hawes, Dr – 20,27
Hayes, Sir J.M. – 18
Hazlett, Dr & Mrs – 164,165
Heathcote, Francis – 194
Heaton, Dr – 107
Henley, W.E. – 71,72,85
Heripret, Dr – 163
Hermitage, Henry – 87
Herschell, Lord – 90
Heston, Dr – 92
Heston, Dr Charles – 98
Hibbs, Dr R.A. – 137
Hickling, Mr & Mrs R.A. – 133
Hickman, Dr – 63
Hicks, Nurse Alice Elizabeth – 100,101,114
Hilberry, Miss, Matron – 86,91,111,194
Hill, Dr F. Haviland – 95

Hill, Sir Rowland – 62
Hill, S. – 73
Hodgson, Rev. John – 66,71
Hodnutt, Joseph – 107
Hogg, Sister – 113,130,133,135
Holbrook, B. – 27
Holden, Dr Luther – 95
Holdsworth, Sir Frank – 155
Holland, Lord – 49
Holland, Sir Eardley – 114
Holland, Henry – 49
Holland, Samuel – 37
Holland, Thomas – 28
Holman, Dr & Mrs – 164,165
Hooper, R. – 18
Hooper, Capt. S. – 27
Hope, Fanny – 62
Howard, Dr J. Warrington – 95
Howland, Mrs – 109
Howland, Mrs – see Doughty
Howland, Frederick J. – 82,183
Howse, Sir H.G. – 95
Hubbard, Mrs – 133
Hubbard, Rev. H.L. – 111
Hughes, Rev. Charles – 46
Hughes, Brig. Glyn – 146
Hugli, J. – 35
Hulme, N. – 18
Hunt, Dr Thomas – 161,162
Hunter, Dr – 66
Hunter, R.E. – 37
Hutchins, J.F. – 108,114
Hutchinson, Sir Jonathan – 95,104
Hutchison, Sir Robert – 114

Icken, Mrs – 54,55
Illington, Mrs, Matron – see Hilberry
Illington, Capt. E.M. – 91,109,111
Ingley, Rev. H. – 46
Isacke, Col. – 95

Jaccard, Danae – 33
Jaccard, Dr P.F. – 13,33
Jairus' Daughter, – Col. Suppt.
Jarman, Dr Francis – 121
Jarvis, Dr – 120
Jarvis, Dr Daniel – 37
Jebens, Dr, Miss Henrietta – 112
Jenkins, Mrs Thomas – 69
Jenner, Edward – 18,47
Jerrold, Walter – 29
Jersey, Earl of – 94
Joel, Dr – 34
Johnson, Patricia Ingrid – 126

Johnstone, Gen. John Julius – 92
Jones, E. Reginald L. –
  162,164,165,168,169
Jones, Lt. Col. Lewis – 87
Jones, Newton – 86
Jones, Sir Robert – 136
Judets, R. & J. – 167
Judkins, George – 103,114

"Kate" – 84
Keate, Thomas – 37
Keeley, Mr – 113
Kempson, Miss, Matron – 105,109,113
Kempson, Miss Joan, Matron – 113,114
Kennedy, Dr – 25
Key, Dr Leonard A. – 139
Khursandi, Dr Diana – 162
Kiewicz, Dr Edmund – 88,91
King Edward VII – 70,93,94,96,99
King Edward VIII – 43,93,123,124
King George III – 124
King George IV – 43
King George V – 103,123
King George VI – 125,126
King Henry I – 29
King, F.H. Bailey – 97
King, Dr Thomas – 120
King's College Hospital – 74
Kirkpatrick, Dr Roger – 148,159
Klugman, David – 162,164,165,169
Knatchbull, Wyndham – 46
Knowles, William – 77
Koch, Robert – 83,87
Kulasinghe, Dr – 159

Lagrange, Dr – 167
Lamb, Charles – 25,41
Lambrinudi, Mr – 114,123
Lane, Sir Arbuthnot – 114
Large, Capt. – 57
Laurence, Sir Trevor – 90,95
Lawrence, Nurse Christina N. – 189,194
Leak, Dr Alison – 179
Leaves (child) – 61
Lefever, John – 63
Legge, William – 61
Lennard, Sir Henry – 82,95,194
Lett, Sir Hugh – 114,177
Lettsom, Mary – 13
Lettsom, William Garrow – 74
Lewin, Dr – 159
Lewis, Hardwicke – 29
Lievesley, Mr – 57,58,59,60,61
Lipscomb, Dr Paul – 172

212

Mayo Clinic – 172
Medical Electricity – 98
Medical Protection Society – 167
Medical Research Council – 176,177
Medical Society of London –
15,16,18,85,93,160,161,162,163
Medley Picture – 16,18,93
Memorial Hall, Wallis – 181,183
Menu – 131,163
Mercers' Company – 114
Mercy – Col. Suppt.
Metropole Hotel – 90
Middlesex Hospital – 75,185
Minutes, Original – 20-24
Miracles – Col. Suppt.
Mirror, Daily – 126
Mons – 107
"Mr Punch" – 116
Museum, Hunterian – 83,84

N.H.S. – 31,84,96,103,113,120,144,
169,170,171,185
Natal – 173
New Brunswick – 108
New Zealand Travelling Fellows – 153
Nitrous Oxide – 63,85
Norwegian Mother – 75
Nurses' Home – 110 & Picture of Statue
of Erasmus Wilson
Nurses' Pay – 93
Nurses' Recreation Hall – 181

Oberammergau – 114
Occupational Therapy – 106
Occupations – 63
Odelca Machine – 176
Olga, s.s. – 75
Operating Theatres – 101,155,157,180,187
& Col. Suppt.
"Operation" – 71
Opium – 80
Oration – 15,85
Orbe – 13,33
Organ – 79,85,172
Orthopaedic Nurses – 158,159,166
Orthopaedic Nursing Certificate (O.N.C.)
– 149,151,166
Orthopaedic Staff Conference – 151,166
Orthopaedic Unit – 147,169
"Other Side of the Lantern" – 70
Out Patients – 46
Oxford – 56,57,65,87,96,126,150

P.A.S. – 135
P.R.C.O.G. – 114
P.R.C.P. – 66,89,114
P.R.C.S. – 41,43,66,75,83,114,177
Paget's Disease – 83
Palsy – 81 & Col. Suppt.
Paraplegia – 142
Pasteurisation – 145
Patronage, Royal –
25,43,91,103,123,124,125,149,150,171
Pegwell Bay – 46,162
Penicillin – 135
Penny Black Stamp – 62
Pewter Plates – 53,54
Pharpar – 81
Philanthropist – 13
Physical Medicine – 66,98,179
Physiotherapists – 87,158,159
Plan of the Hospital, Original – 27
Plaster Beds – see Beds, plaster
Pool of Bethesda – 79,81 & Col. Suppt.
Pool of Siloam – 79,81 & Col. Suppt.
Poppies – 80
Post-Conference Tours – 163,164,165
Post, Penny – 62
Price of Site – 25
Princess Mary's Hospital, Cliftonville –
139,179
Prison Reform – 13
Prittlewell – 28
Procession – 26,28
Promenade – 93
Prontosil – 137
Provisions – 53
Prudence – Col. Suppt.
Puerperal Fever – 89
Pulmonary Consumption – 102,175
Pump – 66,77

Quakers – 13,17,19,161,162
Queen Mary's Hospital, Carshalton –
136,139
Queen of the Channel – 157
Queensland – 108,118
Quinquennial Governor – 97

R.R.C. – 105,109
R.S.P.C.A. – 172
Rabbits – 133
Radcliffe Infirmary – 56,57,65,87,126,150
Radio, Hospital – 113
Radiologist – 121,148

214

Railway Company − 90
Ramsgate − 46
"Receptacle for . . . the Poor" − 21
Records lost − 31,94,128 & Col. Suppt.
Recreation Hall − 181
Red Rover − 57,61
Regent's Canal − 66
Regent's Pavilion − 49
Rehabilitation − 93
Renal Colic − 139
Resident Surgeon's Reports − 65,85,86
Rheumatology − 175 ff
Robert Jones & Agnes Hunt Hospital,
    Oswestry − 136
Rover Scouts − 109
Royal Adelaide − 59
Royal Berkshire Hospital − 87
Royal Colleges − 41,66,75,83,188
Royal Daffodil − 157
Royal Family − 171
Royal George − 62
Royal Hotel − 39
Royal Humane Society − 13,66
Royal Masonic Hospital − 144
Royal National Orthopaedic Hospital − 185
Royal Patronage − *see* Patronage, Royal
Royal Salop Infirmary − 100,102
Royal Society, Fellow of − 35,75
Royal Society of Medicine − 15,159,161,167
Rules for Nurses − 105
Russian Doctor − 155
Rye − 80

S.E.Met.R.H.B. − 91,146,180
Sacro-iliac Tuberculosis − 142,147
St Bartholomew's Fair − 29
St Bartholomew's Hospital − 93,156
St George's Hospital − 29,105
St John's Ambulance Class − 86
St Luke − 79 & Col. Suppt.
St Luke's Hospital, Lowestoft −
    102,103,121,136
St Mark − Col. Suppt.
St Marylebone Hospital − 113
St Nicholas-at-Wade − 98
St Pancras Infirmary − 75
St Stephen − 80
St Thomas' Hospital − 64,150
St Vincent's Hospital − 144
Salk Vaccine − 167
Sanatorium − 175
Scarborough − 16,17
School − 106,108,147

Schoolmaster − 72,88
Scorbutic − 54
Scrofula − 19,40,41,43,51,54,67,87
Sea Wall − 93
Seabrook − 28
Secretary − 159
Senior Registrars' Rotation − 74,168
Sheerness − 157
Sheppey − 157
Silver Medal − 66
Sinus − 74,137,138,142,143
Siummond's F.R.Trust − 98
Smithfield − 29
Snow − 121
Solaria − 25,104,138,170
Soldiers − 107,109,127
Solganol-B-oleosum − 138
South Africa − 153,169,173
South African Orthopaedic Association −
    155,172
South African Travelling Fellows − 153
South-East Kent − 171
South Hill Park − 128
Southend − 29,157
Spine − 54,116
Splint Shops − 111,182,183 & Col. Suppt.
Splintage − 138 & Col. Suppt.
Stamps − 62,161,162
Staphylococcus − 170
Steward − 37,45,57,62,65
Streptomycin − 135
Sulphonamides − 137
Sun Bathing − 115,116,117
Sweetness − 73,74
Swimming Bath − 104
Syria − 80
Syrus − 120

II Kings, 5:1-15 − 80
2LO − 113
Tea Drinking − 13
Temperance − Col. Suppt.
Thalassotherapy − 122
Thames Estuary − 46,157
Thanet Education Committee − 147
Theatre Nurses − 100,101,159
Theatre Sister − 156
Theatres − *see* Operating Theatres
Thermometer, Clinical − 70
Tortola − 13,161
Trades Union Hospital − 144
Transvaal − 173
Travelling Fellows − 153
Treasurer − 37,45

215

WARDS

216